C000077016

Essential Maths

Book 7H

Answers

Elmwood Education

First published 2008

Elmwood Education
Unit 5
Mallow Park
Watchmead
Welwyn Garden City
Herts. AL7 1GX
Tel. 01707 333232

All rights reserved. No part of this publication may be reproduced, stored in a retrieval system, or transmitted, in any form or by any means, electronic, mechanical, photocopying, recording or otherwise, without permission in writing from the publisher or under licence from the Copyright Licensing Agency, Saffron House, 6-10 Kirby Street, London EC1N 8TS.

Any person who commits any unauthorized act in relation to this publication may be liable to criminal prosecution and civil claims for damages.

© David Rayner, Michael White
The moral rights of the authors have been asserted.
Database right Elmwood Education (maker)

ISBN 9781 902 214 825

Printed in Great Britain by Face Communications
www.facecommunications.co.uk

Unit 1

Page 1   Exercise 1M

1. (a) 3000   (b) 90   (c) 70 000

2. (a) 85 707   (b) 86 607   (c) 85 617   (d) 95 607   (e) 85 608   (f) 185 607

3. (a) 299   (b) 6699   (c) 4490   (d) 490   (e) 6900   (f) 6499

4. (a) 8643   (b) 3468   **5.** (a) 96 540   (b) 40 569

6. (a) Six hundred and seventy-five thousand one hundred

7. (a) 98 643   (b) 34 698   **8.** (a) 4 ☐ 0.   (b) 46 000.   **9.** 10

10. $a = 100, b = 7$ **11.** $p = 1000, q = 10$ **12.** $2000 + 100 - 63 - 2$

13. (a) 24 785   (b) 47   (c) 574   (d) 258 (any combination of 2,5,8)

14. $c = 1000, d = 100, e = 10$ **15.** $m = 1000, n = 100, x = 4$

16. (a) Four: 1–10–10, 10–1–10, 2–5–10, 5–2–10   (b) One: 19–5–95

Page 3   Exercise 2M

1. 712   **2.** 645   **3.** 1009   **4.** 3529   **5.** 9619   **6.** 29990

7. 411   **8.** 209   **9.** 839   **10.** 187   **11.** 348   **12.** 205

13. 282   **14.** 744   **15.** 14427   **16.** 2070   **17.** 10115   **18.** 1300

19. 690   **20.** 42800   **21.** (a) 497   (b) $53 + 47$ (c) $9 \times 7 + 3 + 4$

Page 4   Exercise 2E

^{1}3	^{2}5	2		^{3}6	^{4}8
^{5}8	1		^{6}1	4	4
5		^{7}4	9	0	
	^{8}1	8			^{9}4
^{10}7	2	8		^{11}9	4
^{12}1	0	1	2		1

Page 4   Exercise 3M

1. 1945 (or 1944)   **2.** 76000   **3.** (a) $9 + 3 \times 4 = 21$ (b) $6 + 12 \div 3 = 10$ (c) $9 - 10 \div 5 = 7$

(d) $6 \div 3 + 2 + 4 = 8$ (e) $8 \div 4 + 4 \times 4 = 18$ **4.** 189   **5.** 98 cm^2

6. 760   **7.** (a) T   (b) T   (c) T   **8.** 20   **9.** 15

10. 49 or 94   **11.** (a) $543 - 62$ (b) $234 - 65$ **12.** (a) 74   (b) 311

(c) 235   (d) 216   (e) 2172   (f) 40   **13.** $6851 + 31$

14. $36057 + 101$ **15.** $54 \times 3 = 162$ **16.** 3 and 18   **17.** 4,6 and 9   **18.** £42.75

Page 6   *Exercise 4M*

1. 9	**2.** 18	**3.** 7	**4.** 5	**5.** 42	**6.** 16	**7.** 2
8. 2	**9.** 80	**10.** 7	**11.** 27	**12.** 0	**13.** 3	**14.** 13
15. 78	**16.** 77	**17.** 28	**18.** 57	**19.** 3	**20.** 1	**21.** 1
22. 5	**23.** 3	**24.** 72	**25.** 5			

Page 6   *Exercise 4E*

1. 5	**2.** 9	**3.** 9	**4.** 36	**5.** 6	**6.** 9	**7.** 8
8. 56	**9.** 15	**10.** 17	**11.** 5	**12.** 10	**13.** 11	**14.** 11
15. 19	**16.** 39	**17.** 16	**18.** 11	**19.** 45	**20.** 262	**21.** 7
22. 8	**23.** 1	**24.** 13	**25.** 6	**26.** 4	**27.** 48	**28.** 88
29. 63	**30.** 84	**31.** 91	**32.** 91			

Page 7   *Exercise 5M*

1. $\times 5$ **2.** $\div 9$ **3.** -2 **4.** $+3$ **5.** $\div 2$ or $\times \frac{1}{2}$

6. $\times 3$ **7.** -15 **8.** $\times 7$ **9.** $\times 8$

10.
$1 \to 7$
$7 \to 13$
$13 \to 19$
$20 \to 26$
$27 \to 33$
$\to \boxed{+6} \to$

11.
$2 \to 8$
$3 \to 12$
$4 \to 16$
$10 \to 40$
$12 \to 48$
$\to \boxed{\times 4} \to$

12.
$12 \to 5$
$7 \to 0$
$18 \to 11$
$20 \to 13$
$33 \to 26$
$\to \boxed{-7} \to$

13.
$0 \to 11$
$3 \to 14$
$12 \to 23$
$20 \to 31$
$39 \to 50$
$\to \boxed{+11} \to$

14.
$3 \to 1$
$9 \to 3$
$12 \to 4$
$15 \to 5$
$60 \to 20$
$\to \boxed{\div 3} \to$

15.
$0 \to 0$
$5 \to 50$
$4 \to 40$
$7 \to 70$
$10 \to 100$
$\to \boxed{\times 10} \to$

Page 8   *Exercise 5E*

1. (a) $+13$ (b) -6 (c) $\times 2$ **2.** $\times 2$ then $+1$ **3.** $\times 3$ then -1

4. 2   **5.** 7   **6.** 5

Page 9   *Exercise 6 M*

1. (a) 5   (b) 4   (c) 2   (d) 8   (e) 9   (f) 8   (g) 10

     (h) 4   (i) 5   (j) 9   (k) 11   (l) 6   (m) 5   (n) 11

     (o) 16   (p) 1   (q) 0   (r) 7   (s) 9   (t) 9

2. (Missing numbers)

     (a) 11   (b) 48   (c) 6   (d) 9   (e) 2   (f) 10

     (g) 81   (h) 49   (i) 56   (j) 8   (k) 72   (l) 2

     (m) 42   (n) 40   (o) 8

3. (a) $15 \div 5 = 3$, $5 \times 3 = 15$, $3 \times 5 = 15$ (b), (c), (d) similarly

4. 40   **5.** 64

Page 9   Exercise 6E

1.

(a)

	9	8	2	7
5	45	40	10	35
4	36	32	8	28
3	27	24	6	21
6	54	48	12	42

(b)

	4	7	3	8
5	20	35	15	40
9	36	63	27	72
6	24	42	18	48
2	8	14	6	16

(c)

	4	5	8	2
3	12	15	24	6
7	28	35	56	14
6	24	30	48	12
9	36	45	72	18

(d)

	4	5	3	8
2	8	10	6	16
9	36	45	27	72
6	24	30	18	48
7	28	35	21	56

(e)

	3	7	4	9
8	24	56	32	72
2	6	14	8	18
5	15	35	20	45
6	18	42	24	54

(f)

	2	5	7	4
9	18	45	63	36
8	16	40	56	32
3	6	15	21	12
6	12	30	42	24

(g)

	2	7	8	3
5	10	35	40	15
4	8	28	32	12
6	12	42	48	18
9	18	63	72	27

(h)

	2	8	6	9
3	6	24	18	27
7	14	56	42	63
5	10	40	30	45
4	8	32	24	36

(i)

	5	6	3	8
7	35	42	21	56
2	10	12	6	16
4	20	24	12	32
9	45	54	27	72

(j)

	9	7	4	8
2	18	14	8	16
5	45	35	20	40
6	54	42	24	48
3	27	21	12	24

(k)

	7	4	5	8
2	14	8	10	16
6	42	24	30	48
9	63	36	45	72
3	21	12	15	24

(l)

	3	2	5	7
4	12	8	20	28
8	24	16	40	56
9	27	18	45	63
6	18	12	30	42

(or)

	3	9	5	7
4	12	36	20	28
8	24	72	40	56
2	6	18	10	14
6	18	54	30	42

2.

(a)

	6	2	7	4	5
8	48	16	56	32	40
3	18	6	21	12	15
9	54	18	63	36	45
7	42	14	49	28	35
5	30	10	35	20	25

(b)

	4	9	7	3	8
6	24	54	42	18	48
7	28	63	49	21	56
3	12	27	21	9	24
5	20	45	35	15	40
4	16	36	28	12	32

(c)

	3	6	4	8	9
7	21	42	28	56	63
8	24	48	32	64	72
5	15	30	20	40	45
9	27	54	36	72	81
3	9	18	12	24	27

Page 10   **Exercise 7M**

1. 33   **2.** 13   **3.** 23   **4.** 12   **5.** 132
6. 12   **7.** 121   **8.** 62   **9.** 16   **10.** 81
11. 339   **12.** 562   **13.** 243   **14.** 145   **15.** 257
16. 232   **17.** (a) $24 \times 4 = 96$ (b) $123 \times 7 = 861$ (c) $9 \times 217 = 1953$ (d) $47 \times 5 = 235$
(e) $326 \times 7 = 2282$ (f) $703 \times 8 = 5624$ **18.** (a) true   (b) true   **19.** 400

Page 11   **Exercise 7E**

1. 257   **2.** 205   **3.** 1296   **4.** 726   **5.** 305   **6.** 1387
7. 5457   **8.** 1754   **9.** 5231   **10.** 698   **11.** 3214   **12.** 2234
13. 435 g   **14.** 42   **15.** 23   **16.** 27   **17.** 23
18. (a) 108, 12, 240, 80   (b) 15, 20, 220, 280   (c) 7, 21, 120, 24

Page 12   **Exercise 8M**

1. 86 r 2   **2.** 178 r 3   **3.** 149 r 1   **4.** 54 r 2   **5.** 64 r 2
6. 41 r 6   **7.** 528 r 2   **8.** 3570 r 1   **9.** 582 r 5   **10.** 426 r 2
11. 501 r 5   **12.** 39 r 1   **13.** 65 r 7   **14.** 832 r 7   **15.** 14285 r 4
16. 536 r 2   **17.** 286 r 5   **18.** 1110 r 8   **19.** 612   **20.** 12080 r 3

Page 12   **Exercise 8E**

1. 17   **2.** 14   **3.** 5   **4.** 34   **5.** 13
6. 26   **7.** 9   **8.** 12   **9.** 19   **10.** 7
11. 115   **12.** 1428   **13.** 55   **14.** (a) 2   (b) 6   (c) 5
15.   **16.** (a) 784×9 (b) 378×7 (c) 456×8
                    (d) $3222 \div 6 = 536$ (e) $4512 \div 8 = 564$

$\times$	2	9	6	3
7	14	63	42	21
5	10	45	30	15
4	8	36	24	12
8	16	72	48	24

Page 14   **Exercise 1M**

1. 864   **2.** 672   **3.** 805   **4.** 1768   **5.** 612   **6.** 1170
7. 972   **8.** 1176   **9.** 900   **10.** 1672   **11.** 4324   **12.** 476
13. 3034   **14.** 1566   **15.** £1260   **16.** €5589   **17.** £7050

Page 15   **Exercise 1E**

1. 3266   **2.** 3528   **3.** 12614   **4.** 4890   **5.** 4992   **6.** 2844
7. 7587   **8.** 5192   **9.** 32292   **10.** 3807   **11.** 69012   **12.** 602 litres
13. 9744   **14.** 1050   **15.** 1848   **16.** 24×35 **17.** 13×425

Page 16   Exercise 2M

1. (a) 482   (b) 54   **2.** 22   **3.** 24   **4.** 32

5. 27   **6.** 37   **7.** 31   **8.** 45   **9.** 14

10. 24   **11.** 23   **12.** 17   **13.** 61   **14.** (a) 544

  (b) 321   (c) 24   (d) 1210   **15.** 65p   **16.** 759

17.

	13	11	25
17	221	187	425
16	208	176	400
22	286	242	550

Page 17   Exercise 2E

1. 32 r 2   **2.** 34 r 5   **3.** 37   **4.** 44 r 8   **5.** 25   **6.** 47

7. 23 r 2   **8.** 23 r 2   **9.** 25   **10.** 12   **11.** 187   **12.** 36

13. 241   **14.** (a) 17   (b) 24   (c) 36   **15.** 1664   **16.** 35

17. 630 cm   **18.** 33   **19.** 34×65 **20.** $63 360

Page 17   Check Yourself Sections 1.1 and 1.2

1. (a) 6 500 000   (b) 406 012   (c) (i) 6407   (ii) 3036   (iii) 5600

2. (a) 6457   (b) 502 351   (c) 4368   (d) 13000   (e) 4688

3. (a) 354   (b) 807   (c) 56 r 3   (d) 348 r 8   (e) 439

4. (a) 62   (b) 75   **5.** (a) 1104   (b) 2331   (c) 29 375

6. (a) 45   (b) 249   **7.** (a) 3306   (b) 26 each, 2 left over

Page 19   Exercise 1M

1. T   **2.** T   **3.** T   **4.** T   **5.** T   **6.** F

7. F   **8.** F   **9.** >   **10.** >   **11.** <   **12.** >

13. =   **14.** =   **15.** >   **16.** =

17. $\dfrac{7}{100}, \dfrac{2}{10}, \dfrac{1}{1000}$ **18.** $\dfrac{3}{10}, \dfrac{6}{1000}, \dfrac{8}{100}$

19. (a) 0.4   (b) 0.7   (c) 0.5   (d) 1.2   (e) 2.3   (f) 2.9

(g) 3.1   **20.** (a) 0.6, 0.7   (b) 0.9, 1.1   (c) 1.6, 2.0   (d) 1.1, 1.3   (e) 1.0, 0.9

21. (a) 1.9   (b) 1   (c) 2.9   (d) 3.6   (e) 4.8   (f) 6.8

(g) 0.4   (h) 3.9   (i) 3.4   (j) 0.8   (k) 13.1   (l) 1

22. (a) 0.3   (b) 0.07   (c) 0.11   (d) 0.004   (e) 0.16   (f) 0.016

Page 20   Exercise 2M

1. 0.12, 0.21, 0.31   **2.** 0.04, 0.35, 0.4   **3.** 0.67, 0.672, 0.7

4. 0.045, 0.05, 0.07   **5.** 0.089, 0.09, 0.1   **6.** 0.57, 0.705, 0.75

7. 0.041, 0.14, 0.41   **8.** 0.8, 0.809, 0.81   **9.** 0.006, 0.059, 0.6

10. 0.143, 0.15, 0.2   **11.** 0.04, 0.14, 0.2, 0.53   **12.** 0.12, 0.21, 1.12, 1.2

13. 0.08, 0.75, 2.03, 2.3   **14.** 0.26, 0.3, 0.602, 0.62   **15.** 0.5, 1.003, 1.03, 1.3

16. 0.709, 0.79, 0.792, 0.97   **17.** 52 cm, 152cm, 5.2m   **18.** 75p, £0.8, £1.20

19. 200m, $\frac{1}{2}$ km, 0.55 km   **20.** 0.1cm, 1.2mm, 2mm   **21.** My birthday is

22. (a) 3.37   (b) 14.9   (c) 0.941   **23.** (a) 11.26   (b) 1.304   (c) 0.392

24. (a) 3.143   (b) 2.719   (c) 1.415   **25.** (a) £0.11   (b) £0.02   (c) £0.05

(d) £0.10   (e) £0.20   (f) £0.50

Page 22   **Exercise 2E**

1. 46   **2.** 2.6   **3.** 14.8   **4.** 15.2   **5.** 0.2   **6.** 3.2

7. 7   **8.** 5.2   **9.** 3.14   **10.** 0.02   **11.** 1.02   **12.** 0.8

13. 0.24   **14.** 120   **15.** 1.8   **16.** 16   **17.** 88   **18.** 4.35

19. 2.75   **20.** 3.55   **21.** 0.16   **22.** 72.5   **23.** 18.3   **24.** 3.13

Page 22   **Exercise 3M**

1. 7.8   **2.** 1.3   **3.** 8.5   **4.** 20.0   **5.** 15.1   **6.** 23.4

7. 16.5   **8.** 1.5   **9.** 4.2   **10.** 3.7   **11.** 4.7   **12.** 5.3

13. 5.26   **14.** 7.27   **15.** 16.59   **16.** 2.128   **17.** 13.045   **18.** 40.554

19. 21.67   **20.** 12.45   **21.** 465.601   **22.** 44.321   **23.** 13.852   **24.** 19.77

25. 15.6   **26.** 24.4   **27.** 51.9   **28.** 5.3   **29.** 2.41   **30.** 19.78

31. 88.73   **32.** 1.556   **33.** 24.084   **34.** 1.728   **35.** 0.986   **36.** 8.26

37. 7.82 + 1.45 = 9.27   **38.** 3.65 + 0.25 = 3.90   **39.** 5.37 + 3.54 = 8.91

40. 8.27 + 0.74 = 9.01   **41.** 6.86 + 2.17 = 9.03   **42.** 6.95 + 2.26 = 9.21

Page 23   **Exercise 3E**

1. 1.61m   **2.** 7.55m   **3.** £1   **4.** £1,50p, 20p, 5p, 2p, 1p   **5.** £36.10

6. £9.54   **7.** £12.37   **8.** £1, 20p, 10p, 5p, 2p   **9.** £17.30   **10.** £3.86

11. 8.56 − 4.83 = 3.73   **12.** 4.07 + 4.96 = 9.03   **13.** 3.176 − 2.428 = 0.748

14. 8.78 + 0.88 = 9.66   **15.** 5.92 − 2.26 = 3.66   **16.** 2.457 + 4.348 = 6.805

17. 0.01   **18.** 0.002   **19.** (a) 1.272   (b) 9.012   (c) 11.819   (d) 8.678

(e) 6.532   (f) 41.04   (g) 0.273   (h) 0.05   (i) 11.612

20. RELATION   **21.** (a) 8.7   (b) 6.6

22.

	3.2	0.54	0.9	1.8
2.7	5.9	3.24	3.6	4.5
8.6	11.8	9.14	9.5	10.4
0.04	3.24	0.58	0.94	1.84
8	11.2	8.54	8.9	9.8

23. (a) 1.5, 15, 5.3, 5.9, 11.2   (b) 0.59, 0.7, 0.63, 7.63, 2.43

Page 25 **Exercise 4M**

1. 42.3	**2.** 56.3	**3.** 42.7	**4.** 463	**5.** 0.75	**6.** 0.63
7. 1147	**8.** 10 700	**9.** 633	**10.** 71.4	**11.** 636	**12.** 81.42
13. 7100	**14.** 8900	**15.** 1200	**16.** 130	**17.** 7000	**18.** 92 000
19. 70	**20.** 50 000	**21.** 100	**22.** 5.5	**23.** 0.052	**24.** 180
25. 1000	**26.** 400	**27.** 1	**28.** 0.117	**29.** 0.002	**30.** F
31. 5.72	**32.** 8.92	**33.** 0.53	**34.** 0.471	**35.** 1.412	**36.** 1.93
37. 15.18	**38.** 0.047	**39.** 0.0252	**40.** 0.063	**41.** 0.472	**42.** 0.0279
43. 0.0062	**44.** 1.987	**45.** 4.7	**46.** 0.416		

Page 26 **Exercise 5M**

1. 10.2	**2.** 6.9	**3.** 14.8	**4.** 28.0	**5.** 36.78
6. 71.54	**7.** 42.72	**8.** 11.61	**9.** 4.41	**10.** 8.712
11. 0.666	**12.** 56.5	**13.** 68	**14.** 0.37	**15.** 13.32
16. 92.4	**17.** (a) 1.2	(b) 7	(c) 0.4	(d) 0.2
(e) 0.5	(f) 0.02	**18.** £27.80	**19.** £21.90	**20.** 6.75kg

Page 27 **Exercise 5E**

1. (a) 25.4   (b) 6.48   (c) 10.15   (d) 12   (e) 510
2. (a) 4.4, 44, 0.44   (b) 2.8, 8.4, 84   (c) 7.5, 22.5, 2250   (d) 0.32, 32, 16
3. £12.78   **4.** £119.96   **5.** £9.52   **6.** £13.77   **7.** £12.50   **8.** £62.10
9. 14.08   **10.** (a) £116   (b) £116 000   **11.** £6.35   **12.** £7.47   **13.** £12.64
14. £6.54   **15.** (a) $717.50 (b) 100 000   **16.** £25.80   **17.** (a) 16.2   (b) 437.4
18. £2.65, £2.25 **19.** 55cm^2 **20.** True

Page 28 **Exercise 6M**

1. 4.21	**2.** 34.2	**3.** 4.63	**4.** 0.712	**5.** 47.2
6. 6.31	**7.** 6.24	**8.** 54.14	**9.** 1.34	**10.** £1.52

11.

Page 29 **Exercise 6E**

1. 5.63cm	**2.** £8.47	**3.** (a) 2.24	(b) 2.2525	(c) 1.5125
(d) 0.205	(e) 3.4	(f) 2.75	**4.** 0.928kg	**5.** £3.73
6. 5.64 litres	**7.** 16	**8.** £0.99	**9.** 0.26m	**10.** 25g
11. (a) 3.4	(b) 4.32	(c) 3.6	(d) 3.12	(e) 7.2
12. 1.96m^2	**13.** £31.92			

Page 30 **Exercise 7M**

1. 0.08	**2.** 0.18	**3.** 0.16	**4.** 0.012	**5.** 2.1	**6.** 0.014
7. 0.45	**8.** 0.24	**9.** 0.002	**10.** 0.49	**11.** 0.8	**12.** 4.2
13. 0.45	**14.** 0.016	**15.** 0.0006	**16.** 0.66	**17.** 0.36	**18.** 0.64
19. 0.56	**20.** 1.05	**21.** (a) 0.84m^2	(b) 0.49cm^2	(c) 0.54cm^2	**22.** 0.9 m^2

Page 31 **Exercise 7E**

1. (a) 1.2	(b) 0.1	(c) 100	(d) 0.2	(e) 0.8	(f) 100
2. 1.083	**3.** 1.26	**4.** 0.217	**5.** 0.0084	**6.** 0.0066	**7.** 0.324
8. 0.5677	**9.** 12.96	**10.** 0.253	**11.** 9.27	**12.** 0.04	**13.** 0.16
14.			**15.** £1.43	**16.** €50.41	**17.** 0.8281 m^2

14.

×	0.1	0.02	0.5	8
3	0.3	0.06	1.5	24
0.2	0.02	0.004	0.1	1.6
2.1	0.21	0.042	1.05	16.8
10	1	0.2	5	80

Page 32 **Hidden words**

1. SOLEIL IS SUN IN FRENCH
2. BEAVERS CUT DOWN TREES
3. CAN YOU FIND THE HIDDEN WORDS
4. MY CAT CHASES ONLY MICE

Page 35 **Exercise 1M**

1. 11	**2.** 1	**3.** – 5	**4.** 12	**5.** 21	**6.** 2
7. 17	**8.** 24	**9.** 9	**10.** 30	**11.** 30	**12.** 25
13. 8	**14.** 5	**15.** 6	**16.** 8	**17.** 8	**18.** 3
19. 7	**20.** – 2	**21.** – 4	**22.** 14	**23.** 13	**24.** 0
25. 52	**26.** 11	**27.** 10	**28.** 20	**29.** 5	**30.** 5

31. (a) $4 \times 4 - 7 = 9$ (b) $20 - 3 \times 5 = 5$ (c) $24 \div 3 - 4 = 4$

    (d) $(10 - 1) \times 4 = 36$ (e) $26 - (10 - 3) = 19$ (f) $36 \div (7 - 1) = 6$

    (g) $(6 + 7) \times 5 = 65$ (h) $11 - 12 \div 2 = 5$ (i) $9 + 7 \times 3 = 30$

    (j) $44 + (24 \div 2) = 56$ (k) $(3 \times 7) - 21 = 0$ (l) $48 \div 8 + 11 = 17$

Page 36 *Exercise 1E*

1. 15	**2.** 10	**3.** 5	**4.** 9	**5.** 11	**6.** 1
7. 7	**8.** 0	**9.** 8	**10.** 4	**11.** 0	**12.** 1
13. 18	**14.** 18	**15.** 12	**16.** 27	**17.** 8	**18.** 6
19. 1	**20.** 22	**21.** 9	**22.** 0	**23.** 5	**24.** 0
25. 20	**26.** 10	**27.** 16	**28.** 52	**29.** 40	**30.** 111
31. 51	**32.** 30	**33.** 11	**34.** 9	**35.** 28	**36.** 106
37. 54	**38.** 4	**39.** 4	**40.** 153	**41.** 59	**42.** 165
43. 85	**44.** 12	**45.** 33	**46.** 64	**47.** 67	**48.** 1172
49. 52	**50.** 5	**51.** 4	**52.** 16	**53.** 8	**54.** 2

Page 37 *Exercise 2M*

Part A

1. 16	**2.** 27	**3.** 0	**4.** 37	**5.** 8	**6.** 7
7. 12	**8.** 64	**9.** 80	**10.** 18	**11.** 496	**12.** 125
13. 81	**14.** 8	**15.** 27	**16.** 1	**17.** 64	**18.** 64
19. 16	**20.** 10	**21.** 18	**22.** 40	**23.** 24	**24.** 4

Part B

1. $(3 + 4) \times 5 = 35$

2. $6 + (9 \times 7) = 69$

3. $(7 \times 2) + 3 = 17$

4. $(9 + 12) \times 5 = 105$

5. $6 \times (8 - 2) = 36$

6. $(3 \times 8) - 6 = 18$

7. $(19 - 6) \times 3 = 39$

8. $27 - (9 \div 3) = 24$

9. $(51 \div 3) + 4 = 21$

10. $7 \times (24 - 5) = 133$

11. $(6 + 14) \div 2 = 10$

12. $(11 + 6) \times 4 = 68$

13. $(12 \times 8) - (9 \times 7) = 33$

14. $(8 \times 9) - (4 \times 7) = 44$

15. $(5 \times 6 - 4) \div 2 = 13$

16. $(81 \div 9) \times (12 - 4) = 72$

17. $(3 + 5) \times (9 - 7) = 16$

18. $(16 - 10) \div (18 \div 6) = 2$

19. $(6 + 7 - 1) \div 2 = 6$

20. $(5 + 7) \div 3 \times 0 = 0$

Page 38 *Exercise 2E*

1. $(4 + 8) \div 2 = 6$

2. $(5 + 2) \times 3 = 21$

3. $(7 + 2) \div 3 = 3$

4. $(9 - 4) + 2 = 7$

5. $(8 - 4) \times 5 = 20$

6. $(20 - 2) \div 3 = 6$

7. $(7 \times 4) + 2 = 30$

8. $(7 \times 6) - 22 = 20$

9. $(6 \div 3) \times 4 = 8$

10. $40 \div (8 - 3) = 8$

11. $(36 + 4) \div 8 = 5$

12. $(49 \div 7) \times 2 = 14$

13. $21 + 14 - 11 = 24$

14. $(16 \times 3) + 9 = 57$

15. $(12 + 16) \div 4 = 7$

16. $42 + 6 - 24 = 24$

17. $(18 - 13) \times 5 = 25$

18. $40 \div (16 - 6) = 4$

19. $(7 \times 8) - 6 = 50$

20. $(13 \times 4) - 8 = 44$

21. $4 \times (9 \div 3) = 12$

22. $7 \times (9 \div 3) = 21$

23. $(45 \div 3) - 4 = 11$

24. $(121 \div 11) \times 7 = 77$

Page 38 *Exercise 3M*

1. (a) $8 + \dfrac{6}{2}$ (b) $\dfrac{10}{2} + 4$ (c) $12 - \dfrac{8}{2}$ (d) $\dfrac{10}{3+1}$ (e) $\dfrac{12-7}{2}$ (f) $\dfrac{10}{5} - 1$

2. (a) 2 (b) 8 (c) 3 (d) 3 (e) 2 (f) 2

(g) 4   (h) 19   **3.** 4.175   **4.** 15.87   **5.** 3.18   **6.** 5.32

7. 2.31   **8.** 12.71   **9.** 0.5032   **10.** 9   **11.** 6.4   **12.** 0.28

13. 469.65   **14.** 14.01   **15.** 9.94   **16.** 9.084   **17.** 15.63   **18.** 0.56

19. 15.15   **20.** 11.44   **21.** 6.2   **22.** 5.34   **23.** 7.9   **24.** 35.64

25. 14.91   **26.** 0.09   **27.** 13.03   **28.** 4.913   **29.** 18.76   **30.** 4.6

31. 2.11   **32.** 2.7

Page 40   *Exercise 3E*

1. (a) 5   (b) 8   (c) 4   (d) 3   **2.** (a) $17 - (4.2 \times 3) =$

(b) $28 \div (2.41 + 4.59) =$ **3.** 9.05   **4.** 11.36   **5.** 5.7   **6.** 12.4

7. 1.51   **8.** 4.68   **9.** 2.81   **10.** 4.07   **11.** 15   **12.** 2.4

13. 3.712   **14.** 8.4   **15.** 8.2695   **16.** 9.757   **17.** 5.98   **18.** 6.2

19. 17   **20.** 2.1   **21.** C/E, B/D, F/G   **22.** (a) $(9-3) \div (4 + 8) =$

(b) $30 \div (8-3) = + (4 \times 7) =$ **23.** 5.36   **24.** 80.6013   **25.** 7.7721139

26. 16.5649   **27.** 7.3441   **28.** 12.510369   **29.** 64.11   **30.** 1.575757

31. 14.09125   **32.** 2.4900285   **33.** 0.58615004   **34.** 2.6989796   **35.** 86.6484

36. 44.91   **37.** 1.038   **38.** 1.0307143   **39.** 6.266476   **40.** 0.82546816

41. 2.325   **42.** 9.88558   **43.** 13.380645   **44.** 1.5163075

Page 42   *Exercise 4M*

1. 5.1651376   **2.** 1.6886931   **3.** 2.112388   **4.** 0.4923664

5. 4.2583732   **6.** 0.6362010   **7.** 11.785714   **8.** 2.778

9. 10. 9771429   **10.** 1.2347268   **11.** 7.866666   **12.** 7.7327586

13. 2.1890756   **14.** 1.3240152   **15.** 1.8669384   **16.** 7.46

17. 28.8369   **18.** 13.2711   **19.** 70.193   **20.** 30.1365

21. 14.89   **22.** 0.1855319   **23.** 0.3081383   **24.** 9.2775

25. 1.1640816   **26.** 20.395882   **27.** 1.3277801   **28.** 1.1625487

29. 2.51933985   **30.** 1.1955742   **31.** 10.2775037   **32.** 2.33

33. 8.2646520   **34.** 15.3104   **35.** 4.7344674   **36.** 66.24

37. (a) €385   (b) £482   **38.** (a) $24725 m^2$ (b) 2.4725 hectares

39. 84000   **40.** 2003 only

Page 43   *Exercise 4E*

1. OI   **2.** IGLOO   **3.** BOILED   **4.** EGGS   **5.** SELL

6. I   **7.** SIGHED   **8.** HEIDI   **9.** SHELLS   **10.** BIG

11. GOOSE   **12.** EGGS   **13.** GEESE   **14.** SIEGE   **15.** SID

16. HE   **17.** IS   **18.** BIG   **19.** SLOB   **20.** LESLIE

21. HE   **22.** SLOSHED   **23.** BOOZE   **24.** OH   **25.** BOSS

26. HEDGEHOG

Page 44   Check Yourself Sections 1.3 and 1.4

1. (a) (i) 0.0065, 0.007, 0.08, 0.081   (ii) 0.022, 0.2, 0.202, 0.221

  (b) (i) 7.172   (ii) 3.7182   (iii) 0.603

2. (a) 1.642   (b) 51.8   (c) 0.91   (d) 0.322

3. (a) 22.68   (b) 3.54   (c) 0.2   (d) 0.16   (e) 0.0401

4. (a) 2   (b) 19   (c) 7   (d) 120   (e) 3   (f) 45

5. (a) 89.7   (b) 0.808   (c) 6.05   (d) 3.6

6. (a) 11.05   (b) 13.5   (c) 5.44   (d) 3.95

Page 45   Exercise 1M

1. (a) 1   (b) 24   (c) 30   (d) 17   **2.** 5   **3.** 36

4. 32   **5.** $2\frac{1}{2}$ **6.** 9   **7.** 45   **8.** 19   **9.** 30 000

10. 2.5   **11.** 81   **12.** −12   **13.** −3   **14.** 16   **15.** 2

16. $12\frac{1}{2}$

Page 46   Exercise 1E

1. (a) 14   (b) 26   (c) 6   (d) 1.3   (e) 2   (f) 1.1

2. 3   **3.** 2000   **4.** 1.4   **5.** 5   **6.** −1   **7.** 10

8. 0.3   **9.** 20   **10.** 76   **11.** (a) 3, 48   (b) 7, 16   (c) 32, 2

  (d) 9, −6   **12.** 720   **13.** 5×7^2 **14.** $\frac{5}{11}$ **15.** 1440   **16.** (a) 16

  (b) 65

Page 46   Exercise 2M

1. 20, 25, 30, 35, 40   **2.** (a) 8, 10, 12, 14, 16   (b) 100, 96, 92, 88, 84   (c) 10, 20, 40, 80, 160

  (d) 64, 32, 16, 8, 4   **3.** (a) add 7   (b) subtract 11   (c) add 0.2

  (d) multiply by 2   **4.** (a) 47   (b) 3   (c) 25 − 51 − 103 − 207

5. (a) 28   (b) 3   (c) 1 − 1 − 1 − 1   **6.** (a) add $\frac{1}{2}$

  (b) multiply by 2   (c) add 0.1   (d) divide by 3   (e) subtract 0.15

  (f) divide by 2   (g) multiply by 2 and add 2   (h) multiply by 3 and add 1

7. (a) 3, 2.7, 2.4, 2.1, 1.8, 1.5   (b) 864, 144, 24, 4, $\frac{2}{3}$, $\frac{1}{9}$ (c) 27, 38, 49, 60, 71, 82

  (d) 600, 60, 6, 0.6, 0.06, 0.006   (e) 1, 4, 5, 9, 14, 23   (f) 0, 2, 2, 4, 6, 10

  (g) 3, 9, 21, 45, 93, 189   (h) 5, 7, 11, 13, 17, 19   **8.** (b) 4, 12, 24, 40, 60, 84

9. add 2, multiply by 3 (many others)   **10.** −7 or less   **11.** (a) 6561   (b) 177147

Page 48   Exercise 2E

1. (a) 5, 10, 15 etc   (b) (e.g.) 0.1, 5.1, 10.1,...   (c) no

2. (a) 4, 9, 14, 19, 24   (b) 20, 17, 14, 11, 8   (c) 3, 6, 12, 24, 48

(d) 1, 10, 100, 1000, 10 000

(c) 40, 37, 34, 31, 28, 25

(c) 33

3. (a) 2, 5, 8, 11, 14, 17   (b) 10, 14, 18, 22, 26, 30, 34

4. (a) 25   (b) 21

(d) 29

5. (a) $5 \times 999 = 4995$, $6 \times 999 = 5994$, $7 \times 999 = 6993$

(b) $33\,333 \times 5 = 166\,665$, $333\,333 \times 5 = 1\,666\,665$

(c) 1 666 666 665

6. (a) $5^2 + 5 + 6 = 36$, $6^2 + 6 + 7 = 49$, $7^2 + 7 + 8 = 64$

(b) $12^2 + 12 + 13 = 169$

7. (a) $654\,321 \times 9 = 5\,888\,889$ (b) $= 788\,888\,889$

8. (a) $5 + 9 \times 1234 = 11\,111$ (b) $7 + 9 \times 123\,456 = 1\,111\,111$

9. (a) $6 \times 7 = 6 + 6 \times 6$ (b) $10 \times 11 = 10 + 10 \times 10$, $11 \times 12 = 11 + 11 \times 11$

10. $13 + 15 + 17 + 19 = 64 = 4^3$ etc   **11.** (a) 1, 7, 21, 35, 35, 21, 7, 1   (b) 21, 28, 36

(c) 1, 2, 4, 8, 16 etc   (d) $512 (= 2^9)$

12. (a) 7   (b) 63   (c) $1023 (= 2^{10} - 1)$

Page 51   *Exercise 1M*

1.

9	8	6	8	6.7	14
7	3	7	9	2.9	4.5
32	22	26	34	19.2	37

2. (a) 32 m   (b) 16   **3.** 22   **4.** 28

5. 36   **6.** 40   **7.** 36   **8.** 38

9. 42   **10.** 50   **11.** 17 m   **12.** 36 cm

13. (a) B   (b) A and D   **14.** various shapes

15. (a) E   (b) A   (c) B

Page 52   *Exercise 1E*

1. (a) 57 cm²   (b) 94 cm²   **2.** (a) 140 cm²   (b) 132 cm²   (c) 90 cm²

(d) 123 cm²

3. (a) 7 cm   (b) 9.5 cm   (c) 2.4 cm   (d) 9.5 m   **4.** 12 cm

5. (a) 200, 150   (b) 150   **6.** 60 cm   **7.** 48   **8.** 2700   **9.** 3

Page 54   *Exercise 2M*

1. (All cm²) (a) 16   (b) 10.5   (c) 80   (d) 54   (e) 35   (f) 22.5

(g) 30   (h) 96

2.

6	8	14	6	7
4	9	20	30	30
12	36	140	90	105

3. (a) 4.5   (b) 4.5   (c) 3   (d) 3

4. (a) 168 cm²   (b) 90 cm²   (c) 180 cm²

5. (a) 88 cm²   (b) 109 cm²   **6.** 99 m²   **7.** 9 cm

8. (a) 6 cm   (b) 8 cm   (c) 9 cm   (d) 10 cm

9. (a) 39 cm²   (b) 112 cm²

Page 57   *Exercise 2E*

1. (a) $10\frac{1}{2}$ (b) $12\frac{1}{2}$ (c) 14   **2.** (a) 4   (b) $10\frac{1}{2}$

3. (a) $11\frac{1}{2}$ (b) 20   **4.** (a) 30   (b) 43   **5.** $\frac{3}{4}$ cm²   **6.** $\frac{1}{3}$

Page 58 **Exercise 3M**

1. (a) 14 cm² (b) 39 cm² **2.** 71.25 m² **3.** length = 12 cm, width = 8 cm, height = 3 cm
4. 50 **5.** 150 cm² **6.** 10 **7.** 19.5 m²

Page 59 **Exercise 3E**

1. 40 hectares **2.** 140 m **3.** 25 **4.** £28 000 **5.** 810 m **6.** (a) 63 m²

(b) £63.20 **7.** 195 m², £3.90 **8.** £3250 **9.** (a) 4 cm (b) 3 cm **10.** $\frac{5}{9}$ cm

11. 9.11 cm $(= \sqrt{83})$ **12.** (All in cm²) A = 2, B = 6, C = 1, D = 3, E = 3, F = 3, G = 3, H = 2, I = 4

Page 61 **Investigation**

Part D Largest area is a square of side 8 cm
Part E Square of side 25 cm. Area is 625 cm²

Page 61 **Check Yourself on Section 1.6**

1. (a) 62 cm (b) 7 m **2.** (a) 92 cm² (b) 153 m² (c) 248 cm² (d) 7 m
3. (a) 84 cm² (b) 115 cm² (c) 12 cm (d) 10.5 square units

Page 62 **Mixed Review Part one**

1. (a) 236 + 172 (b) 359 + 204 (c) 585 + 178 (d) 349 + 356 (e) 246 + 168
(f) 559 + 294 **2.** (a) 50 − 43 (b) 46 − 38 (c) 86 + 52 (d) 316 − 253
(e) 691 − 278 (f) 474 − 129 **3.** (a) 67 × 2 = 134 (b) 86 × 4 = 344 (c) 57 × 6 = 342
(d) 39 × 3 = 117 (e) 239 × 6 = 1434 (f) 533 × 4 = 2132
4. Missing digits: (a) 5 (b) 2 (c) 6 (d) 5 (e) 4 (f) 8

5.

¹2	²1	³9	■	⁴5	⁵5
⁶6	6	•5	⁷4	■	3
⁸6	•9	■	⁹3	¹⁰7	6
■	■	¹¹3	•6	9	■
¹²4	¹³4	1	■	¹⁴9	¹⁵•7
¹⁶7	5	0	■	¹⁷6	4

Part two

1. List C
2.

	7	4	9	8
(b) 5	35	20	45	40
2	14	8	18	16
6	42	24	54	48
9	63	36	81	72

3. (a) 40
(c) $\frac{1}{3}$, 7

4. (a) 5 × 6 − 6 = 24
(b) 30 − 4 × 7 = 2
(c) 36 ÷ 9 + 7 = 11
(d) (12 − 7) × 4 = 20
(e) 32 − (12 − 8) = 28
(f) 13 − 12 ÷ 2 = 7

	5	9	8	6	4
3	15	27	24	18	12
7	35	63	56	42	28
2	10	18	16	12	8
5	25	45	40	30	20
8	40	72	64	48	32

5. 9.52 **6.** 62.4 **7.** 4.6 **8.** 7.7 **9.** 3.5 **10.** 6.4
11. 4.07 **12.** 4.6 **13.** 15 **14.** 10.65 **15.** 8.4 **16.** 3.2
17. (a) add 5 (b) multiply by 2 (c) take away 6
(d) subtract 0.3 (e) multiply by 3 (f) multiply by 2 and then add 1
18. Not right **19.** (a) 34 m² (b) 26 m **20.** 16 cm² **21.** (c) is correct
22. 12 **23.** 8.5 m **24.** 94 tonnes **25.** 15 **26.** 4 (accept $3\frac{3}{4}$)

Page 66 *Puzzles and Problems 1*

1. (a) A = 7, B = 5, C = 8, D = 10 (b) A = 6, B = 2, C = 5, D = 4, E = 8
(c) A = 6, B = 3, C = 1, D = 5 (d) A = 8, B = 3

2. (a)
$$\begin{array}{r} 314 \\ + 463 \\ \hline 777 \end{array}$$
(b)
$$\begin{array}{r} 354 \\ + 624 \\ \hline 978 \end{array}$$
(c)
$$\begin{array}{r} 358 \\ + 144 \\ \hline 502 \end{array}$$
3. (a)
$$\begin{array}{r} 536 \\ + 214 \\ \hline 750 \end{array}$$
(b)
$$\begin{array}{r} 246 \\ + 357 \\ \hline 603 \end{array}$$
(c)
$$\begin{array}{r} 634 \\ + 284 \\ \hline 918 \end{array}$$

4. (a)
$$\begin{array}{r} 37 \\ \times\ 5 \\ \hline 185 \end{array}$$
(b)
$$\begin{array}{r} 47 \\ \times\ 9 \\ \hline 423 \end{array}$$
(c)
$$\begin{array}{r} 374 \\ \times\ 8 \\ \hline 2992 \end{array}$$

5. (a) $231 \div 7 = 33$ (b) $13 \times 11 = 143$ (c) $12 \times 9 = 108$ (d) $918 \div 6 = 153$

6. (a)
$$\begin{array}{r} 856 \\ - 324 \\ \hline 532 \end{array}$$
(b)
$$\begin{array}{r} 832 \\ - 415 \\ \hline 417 \end{array}$$
(c)
$$\begin{array}{r} 645 \\ - 288 \\ \hline 357 \end{array}$$

7. (a) $55 \times 8 = 440$ (b) $21 \times 11 = 231$ (c) $400 \div 8 = 50$ (d) $978 \div 6 = 163$
8. (a) $79 + 48 = 127$ (b) $512 - 49 = 463$ (c) $653 - 487 = 166$ (d) $875 - 579 = 296$
9. 12 **10.**

E	C	A	D	B
D	B	E	C	A
C	A	D	B	E
B	E	C	A	D
A	D	B	E	C

11. 11 tapes at £7.99: £87.89
12. Three on each side, etc!

Page 67 *Divisibility Investigation*

• if the number ends in Zero ⟨divisible by⟩ 10

TASK A

Number	Divisible by						
	2	3	4	5	6	8	9
363	✗	✓	✗	✗	✗	✗	✗
224	✓	✗	✓	✗	✗	✓	✗
459	✗	✓	✗	✗	✗	✗	✓
155	✗	✗	✗	✓	✗	✗	✗
168	✓	✓	✓	✗	✓	✓	✗
865	✗	✗	✗	✓	✗	✗	✗
360	✓	✓	✓	✓	✓	✓	✓
2601	✗	✓	✗	✗	✗	✗	✓

TASK B   37 177 Yes, 8498 Yes, 431 781 Yes, 42 329 Yes, 39 579 No, 910 987 Yes

Page 68   Mental Arithmetic Test 1

1. 6   **2.** 600   **3.** $\frac{1}{4}$ **4.** 31   **5.** 550 cm   **6.** 9

7. 16   **8.** 27%   **9.** 36 m²   **10.** 8 or 16   **11.** 850   **12.** any multiple of 8

13. 2   **14.** 4.3   **15.** 15   **16.** 14°C   **17.** £1.58   **18.** 20

19. 280   **20.** 120°   **21.** 36   **22.** false   **23.** 8   **24.** $\frac{3}{8}$ **25.** 8

Page 69   Mental Arithmetic Test 2

1. 9   **2.** 184   **3.** 0.75   **4.** 2.4   **5.** 50p, 10p, 5p, 2p

6. £17.97   **7.** 150 mm   **8.** 240   **9.** 30   **10.** 56   **11.** 29p

12. 7.5   **13.** 17:30   **14.** 46°   **15.** 7 cm   **16.** £18.22   **17.** £2.04

18. 8:25   **19.** 60   **20.** 4000 mm   **21.** −4   **22.** 1.25   **23.** 4950

24. $\frac{3}{6}$ **25.** 38p

Page 71   A long time ago! 1

Exercise

2. (a) 1472   (b) 2562   (c) 4144   (d) 38 484   (e) 225 568   (f) 4 791 773

(g) 39 720   (h) 82 449

Unit 2

Page 73 **Exercise 1M**

1. (a) 3   (b) 4 and 7   **2.** (a) 6   (b) 5   (c) 6
3. (a) 3   (b) 2.5   (c) 12   **4.** (a) 10   (b) 20
5. (a) 26   (b) 27   (c) Nina by 1   **6.** 45 700   **7.** (a) 2   (b) 8
8. 165   **9.** 23   **10.** (a) 90   (b) 205   (c) 220   (d) 193
11. (a) 14   (b) 16   (c) 14.8   **12.** (a) 2 modes; 7 and 12   (b) 3, 8 and 12

Page 74 **Exercise 1E**

1. (a) 6   (b) 6.5   **2.** 66 or 5   **3.** 4.5; she wins   **4.** −2°
5. 3, 11   **6.** (a) False   (b) Possible   (c) Possible   **7.** 3
8. (a) 6   (b) 14   **9.** (a) 11, 11, 16, 16, 15   (b) 15   **10.** 3

Page 76 **Exercise 2M**

1. (a) Year 8: mean = 5.2 range = 5   (b) Year 9: mean = 4.7 range = 5
2. (a) Year 7: median = 4 range = 6   (b) Year 11: median = 3 range = 7
3. (a) 1.88 m   (b) 0.34 m   (c) 1.93 m   (d) 0.14 m   (e) Tipperton
4. (a) mean = 4.7 range = 9   (b) mean = 6 range = 10
5. (a) 71s   (b) 8s   (c) 78s   (d) 12s   (e) Helen

Page 78 **Exercise 2E**

1. 2.76   **2.** $\dfrac{(7\times0)+(12\times1)+(11\times2)+(10\times3)}{40}=\dfrac{64}{40}=1.6$ **3.** (a) 3.64   (b) 3.45

4. (a)

goals	0	1	2	3	4	5
frequency	4	8	6	2	3	2

(b) 1   (c) 1.92

5. (a) 1   (b) 6   (c) 1.98   **6.** (a) 3.5   (b) 6

Page 80 **Check Yourself on Section 2.1**

1. (a) 9   (b) 8.5   (c) 8   **2.** 37
3. Warriors: mean = 23.8 range = 14   Sabres: mean = 22.7   range = 12   **4.** (a) 3   (b) 2.6125

Page 81 **Exercise 1M**

1. (a) $\dfrac{12}{16}$ (b) $\dfrac{4}{20}$ (c) $\dfrac{10}{12}$ (d) $\dfrac{4}{5}$ (e) $\dfrac{15}{27}$ (f) $\dfrac{20}{35}$ (g) $\dfrac{9}{24}$ (h) $\dfrac{36}{60}$
(i) $\dfrac{21}{30}$ (j) $\dfrac{25}{40}$ (k) $\dfrac{20}{55}$ (l) $\dfrac{48}{60}$ (m) $\dfrac{4}{5}$ (n) $\dfrac{3}{5}$ (o) $\dfrac{4}{9}$ (p) $\dfrac{7}{10}$

2. (a) $\dfrac{1}{5}$ (b) $\dfrac{4}{5}$ (c) $\dfrac{7}{9}$ (d) $\dfrac{2}{3}$ (e) $\dfrac{3}{5}$ (f) $\dfrac{2}{7}$ (g) $\dfrac{2}{3}$ (h) $\dfrac{1}{4}$
(i) $\dfrac{7}{9}$ (j) $\dfrac{2}{3}$ **3.** Rugby   **4.** Brazil   **5.** Shirt   **6.** Apricot

Page 83 **Exercise 1E**

1. $3\frac{1}{2}$ **2.** $2\frac{2}{3}$ **3.** $1\frac{1}{4}$ **4.** $4\frac{1}{2}$ **5.** 6   **6.** $1\frac{6}{7}$ **7.** $1\frac{3}{8}$ **8.** 4

9. $2\frac{2}{5}$ **10.** $6\frac{3}{4}$ **11.** $3\frac{1}{7}$ **12.** $1\frac{8}{9}$ **13.** $3\frac{5}{6}$ **14.** $7\frac{3}{10}$ **15.** 13   **16.** 31

17. $\frac{7}{3}$ **18.** $\frac{13}{4}$ **19.** $\frac{17}{3}$ **20.** $\frac{27}{4}$ **21.** $\frac{22}{5}$ **22.** $\frac{57}{8}$ **23.** $\frac{26}{5}$ **24.** $\frac{31}{7}$

25. $\frac{16}{3}$ **26.** $\frac{14}{5}$ **27.** $\frac{43}{9}$ **28.** $\frac{67}{10}$ **29.** $\frac{43}{8}$ **30.** $\frac{41}{5}$ **31.** $\frac{67}{9}$

Page 84 **Exercise 2M**

1. (a) 15   (b) 15   (c) 63   (d) 22   (e) 35   (f) 8

(g) 32   (h) 40   **2.** PYRAMID   **3.** (a) 24   (b) 16   (c) 10

(d) 24   (e) 28   (f) 21   (g) 98   (h) 96   **4.** 35

5. 35 litres   **6.** (a) 30 kg   (b) 72 cm   (c) £60   (d) £36   (e) 150 kg

(f) 24 m   (g) 20 cm   (h) 48 m   (i) £148   **7.** (a) 2.8 m or 280 cm

(b) 1.96 m or 196 cm   **8.** (a) 3   (b) 2   (c) 10   (d) 4

(e) 20   (f) 40   **9.** (a) $\frac{1}{2}$ (b) $\frac{3}{4}$ (c) $\frac{1}{8}$

10. (a) 12   (b) 9   **11.** (b) $\frac{1}{2} + \frac{1}{3} + \frac{1}{6}$ **12.** $49\frac{3}{4}$

Page 87 **Exercise 2E**

1. $\frac{4}{7}$ **2.** $\frac{5}{8}$ **3.** $\frac{3}{7}$ **4.** $\frac{1}{8}$ **5.** $\frac{1}{8}$ **6.** $\frac{9}{10}$ **7.** $\frac{1}{4}$ **8.** $\frac{1}{6}$

9. $\frac{3}{4}$ **10.** $\frac{1}{10}$ **12.** $\frac{17}{20}$ **13.** $\frac{5}{12}$ **14.** $\frac{2}{21}$ **15.** $\frac{31}{40}$ **16.** $\frac{11}{90}$ **17.** $\frac{5}{24}$

18. $\frac{43}{60}$ **19.** $\frac{59}{63}$ **20.** $\frac{29}{45}$ **21.** $\frac{1}{30}$ **22.** (a) $\frac{11}{12}$ (b) $\frac{3}{20}$ (c) $\frac{2}{15}$

23. (a) $\frac{8}{15}$ (b) $\frac{7}{15}$ **24.** (a) $2\frac{1}{8}$ (b) $2\frac{11}{12}$ (c) $1\frac{29}{40}$ **25.** $2\frac{1}{12}$ **26.** $2\frac{7}{15}$

27. $1\frac{5}{8}$ **28.** $1\frac{5}{12}$ **29.** $4\frac{7}{20}$ **30.** $1\frac{19}{24}$ **31.** $1\frac{7}{10}$ **32.** $3\frac{37}{40}$ **33.** $6\frac{11}{15}$ m   **34.** $\frac{8}{15}$

35. Many answers, eg. $\frac{1}{2} + \frac{4}{8}, \frac{1}{5} + \frac{8}{10}$, etc.   **36.** 300 ml   **37.** (a) 28 000 gallons   (b) 16 800 gallons

38. (a) £36 000   (b) £49 500

Page 89 **Exercise 1M**

1. 0.35   **2.** $\frac{15}{100} = 0.15$ **3.** $\frac{8}{10} = 0.8$ **4.** $\frac{1}{4} = 0.25$ **5.** $\frac{6}{10} = 0.6$

6. $\frac{16}{100} = 0.16$ **7.** 0.55   **8.** 0.4   **9.** 0.28   **10.** 0.75

11. 0.85   **12.** 0.92   **13.** 0.76   **14.** 0.75   **15.** 0.6

16. 0.25   **17.** 0.001111111

Page 90   *Exercise 1E*

1. 0.3, $\frac{9}{25}$, $\frac{8}{20}$ **2.** $\frac{3}{5}$, 0.7, $\frac{3}{4}$ **3.** 0.7, $\frac{12}{16}$, $\frac{4}{5}$ **4.** $\frac{1}{20}$, 0.15, $\frac{1}{5}$ **5.** 0.019

6. 0.008   **7.** 0.136   **8.** 0.75   **9.** 0.075   **10.** 0.028

11. 0.25   **12.** 0.178   **13.** 0.012   **14.** 0.0173

Page 90   *Exercise 2M*

1. $\frac{3}{10}$ **2.** $\frac{7}{10}$ **3.** $\frac{1}{100}$ **4.** $\frac{9}{100}$ **5.** $\frac{13}{100}$ **6.** $\frac{51}{100}$

7. $\frac{69}{100}$ **8.** $\frac{9}{10}$ **9.** $\frac{23}{100}$ **10.** $\frac{37}{100}$ **11.** $\frac{89}{100}$ **12.** $2\frac{3}{10}$

13. $4\frac{73}{100}$ **14.** $5\frac{1}{100}$ **15.** $6\frac{7}{10}$

Page 91   *Exercise 2E*

1. same amount   **2.** $\frac{4}{5}$ **3.** $\frac{1}{20}$ **4.** $\frac{2}{25}$ **5.** $\frac{1}{4}$ **6.** $\frac{6}{25}$

7. $\frac{1}{50}$ **8.** $\frac{2}{5}$ **9.** $\frac{8}{25}$ **10.** $\frac{3}{20}$ **11.** $\frac{9}{50}$ **12.** $\frac{3}{4}$

13. $3\frac{1}{5}$ **14.** $4\frac{1}{2}$ **15.** $\frac{14}{25}$ **16.** $6\frac{1}{25}$ **17.** $7\frac{3}{25}$ **18.** $3\frac{3}{4}$

19. $8\frac{3}{5}$ **20.** $2\frac{19}{20}$ **21.** $4\frac{9}{25}$

Page 92   *Exercise 3M*

1. (a) $\frac{2}{5}$ (b) $\frac{7}{100}$ (c) $\frac{11}{50}$ (d) $\frac{4}{5}$ (e) $\frac{1}{20}$ (f) $\frac{89}{100}$

(g) $\frac{1}{10}$ (h) $\frac{7}{25}$ (i) $\frac{1}{25}$ (j) $\frac{7}{20}$

2. (a) 40%   (b) 45%   (c) $\frac{12}{100}$ = 12%   (d) $\frac{55}{100}$ = 55%

(e) $\frac{90}{100}$ = 90%   (f) $\frac{38}{100}$ = 38%   **3.** (a) 85%   (b) 52%   (c) 92%

4. $\frac{3}{20}$ **5.** $\frac{16}{25}$ **6.** 4%   **7.** 80%   **8.** (a) true   (b) false

(c) true   (d) false   (e) true   (f) true   **9.** $\frac{37}{50}$, $\frac{3}{4}$, $\frac{39}{50}$

Page 93   *Exercise 3E*

1. (a) $\frac{37}{100}$ = 37%   (b) $\frac{17}{100}$ = 17%   (c) $\frac{3}{100}$ = 3%   (d) $\frac{40}{100}$ = 40%   **2.** (a) 0.29

(b) 0.52   (c) 0.8   (d) 0.06   (e) 0.03   (f) 0.13

(g) 1.3   (h) 2.4

3.

$\frac{3}{10}$	0.3	30%
$\frac{11}{20}$	0.55	55%
$\frac{3}{25}$	0.12	12%
$\frac{1}{20}$	0.05	5%
$\frac{12}{25}$	0.48	48%

4. (a) MATHS IS NOT HARD

(b) DECIMALS MAKE SENSE

(c) I CAN SOLVE PROBLEMS

Page 94   Investigation – Escape

(a) 3 prisoners; 1, 4, 9   (b) 10 prisoners; 1, 4, 9, 16, 25, 36, 49, 64, 81, 100   (c) 31 prisoners

Page 95   Check Yourself on Sections 2.2 and 2.3

1. (a) $\frac{7}{42}$ (b) $\frac{28}{36}$ (c) $\frac{2}{3}$ (d) $\frac{49}{56}$, $\frac{63}{72}$

2. (a) 20   (b) 42   (c) 49   **3.** (a) $\frac{29}{35}$ (b) $\frac{1}{12}$ (c) $2\frac{13}{40}$

(d) $3\frac{11}{12}$ **4.** 40%, 0.4, $\frac{2}{5}$;   75%, 0.75, $\frac{3}{4}$;   5%, 0.05, $\frac{1}{20}$;   45%, 0.45, $\frac{9}{20}$

Page 96   Exercise 1M

1. EF̂G or GF̂E   **2.** WX̂Y or YX̂W   **3.** MN̂P or PN̂M   **4.** (a) 65°   (b) 115°

5. (a) 110°   (b) 55°   (c) 110°   (d) 125°

6. (a) 68°   (b) 63°   **7.** (a) CÊD or DÊC   (b) BÂE or EÂB or BÂC or CÂB

(c) AD̂E or ED̂A or AD̂B or BD̂A   (d) AĈD or DĈA or EĈD or DĈE

(e) CB̂E or EB̂C or CB̂D or DB̂C

Page 97   Exercise 1E   [Apologies : The diagram is not accurate!]

1. 20°	**2.** 40°	**3.** 60°	**4.** 72°	**5.** 10°	**6.** 45°
7. 65°	**8.** 80°	**9.** 36°	**10.** 23°	**11.** 14°	**12.** 28°
13. 126°	**14.** 135°	**15.** 170°	**16.** 6°	**17.** 30°	**18.** 174°
19. 166°	**20.** 160°	**21.** 157°	**22.** 150°	**23.** 144°	**24.** 53°
25. 115°	**26.** 155°	**27.** 97°	**28.** 108°	**29.** 120°	**30.** 127°
31. 25°	**32.** 83°	**33.** 91°	**34.** 107°	**35.** 140°	**36.** 54°
37. 73°	**38.** 89°	**39.** 152°	**40.** 100°		

Page 98   Exercise 2M

1. 48°	**2.** 63°	**3.** 46°	**4.** 59°	**5.** 52°	**6.** 134°

7. (a) 76°   (b) 128°   (c) 93°   **8.** (a) 68°   (b) 127°   (c) 93°

10. (a) acute   (b) acute   (c) obtuse   (d) obtuse   (e) acute   (f) acute

(g) reflex   (h) obtuse   (i) reflex   (j) obtuse

Page 99 **Exercise 2E**

1. 35°	**2.** 38°	**3.** 42°	**4.** 133°	**5.** 112°	**6.** 23°
7. 112°	**8.** 35°	**9.** $94\frac{1}{2}°$	**10.** 121°	**11.** 100°	**12.** 66°
13. 103°	**14.** 24°	**15.** $45\frac{1}{2}°$	**16.** 65°		

Page 100 **Exercise 3M**

1. 40° **2.** 51° **3.** 60° **4.** 25° **5.** 137° **6.** 60°
7. 42° **8.** h = 125°, i = 55° **9.** 93° **10.** 153°
11. l = 153°, m = 153°, n = 27° **12.** p = 90°, q = 90°, r = 90°

Page 100 **Exercise 3E**

1. a = 60° **2.** b = 40° **3.** c = 75° **4.** d = 105° **5.** e = 88° **6.** f = 80°
7. g = 47° **8.** h = 54° **9.** i = 33° **10.** j = 47° **11.** k = 60°, 2k = 120°, 3k = 180°
12. m = 25°, 3m = 75°

Page 102 **Exercise 4M**

1. 65° **2.** 39° **3.** c = 84°, d = 96° **4.** e = 110° **5.** f = 66°
6. g = 105° **7.** h = 86° **8.** i = 66° **9.** j = 120° **10.** k = 162° **11.** l = 48°
12. m = 70°, n = 40° **13.** p = 45° **14.** q = 60° **15.** r = 72°
16. s = 65°, t = 65°, u = 50°

Page 102 **Exercise 4E**

1. a = 28° **2.** b = 286° **3.** c = 62°, d = 56° **4.** e = 38°, f = 109°
5. g = 40° **6.** h = 34° **7.** i = 72°, j = 36° **8.** 2k = 36°, 3k = 54°, 5k = 90°
9. l = 36°, 2l = 72° **10.** m = 30°, 2m = 60°, m + 120° = 150°, n = 90°
11. p = 68° **12.** q = 115°, q − 50° = 65°, q − 70° = 45°, r = 20° **13.** 128°
14. 70° **15.** Slab B

Page 105 **Exercise 5M**

1. a = 53°, b = 53°, c = 127° **2.** d = 116°, e = 116°, f = 64° **3.** g = 125°, h = 125°, i = 55°
4. j = 131°, k = 49°, l = 131° **5.** m = 54°, n = 54° **6.** p = 74°, q = 135°, r = 45°
7. s = 37°, t = 143°, u = 45° **8.** v = 69°, w = 111°, x = 78°, y = 102° **9.** a = 38°, b = 52°
10. c = 70°, d = 48°, e = 62° **11.** f = 28°, g = 115°, h = 37° **12.** i = 70°, j = 32°, k = 78°

Page 106 **Exercise 5E**

1. a = 91° **2.** b = 83° **3.** c = 73° **4.** d = 128° **5.** e = 122°
6. f = 68°, g = 115° **7.** h = 78° **8.** i = 65° **9.** j = 119° **10.** k = 112°
11. l = 84° **12.** m = 98° **13.** n = 20°, 4n = 80° **14.** p = 40°, 2p = 80° **15.** q = 24°
16. r = 71° **17.** s = 50° **18.** t = 34° **19.** u = 92° **20.** v = 72°
21. w = 46°

Page 107   ***Check Yourself on Section 2.4***

1. (a) 85°   (b) 30°   (c) 100°   **2.** (a) 62°   (b) 115°   **3.** (a) 65°
     (b) 125°   (c) $X\hat{W}Y = 100°$, $V\hat{W}X = 80°$ **4.** (a) 28°   (b) 102°   (c) 121°
5. (a) $B\hat{E}F = 78°$, $F\hat{E}H = 102°$ (b) 61°   **6.** (a) 103°   (b) 85°

Page 109   ***Exercise 1M***

1. $d - 9$ **2.** $2x$ **3.** $y + 25$ **4.** $\dfrac{m}{6}$ **5.** $2k - 8$ **6.** $3M - 4$

7. $25p$ **8.** $2w + 15$ **9.** $10q - 8$ **10.** $\dfrac{n}{3} + 5$ **11.** $3b + 8$ **12.** $\dfrac{y}{8} - 7$

13. $\dfrac{3f}{10}$ **14.** $p = 4y$ **15.** $3a$ **16.** $5m$ **17.** $8h$ **18.** $2x + 2y$

19. $2w + 6$ **20.** $2b + c$

Page 111   ***Exercise 1E***

1. $2x + y$ **2.** $3s - w$ **3.** $4x - y + 5$ **4.** $\dfrac{n}{5} - 3$ **5.** $g - f + n$ **6.** $2y + 3w - x$

7. $4(p + q)$ **8.** $6m + 3n$ **9.** $5q - 3p + 4m$ **10.** $\dfrac{2n}{9} + 6$ **11.** $5x$ **12.** $y + 20$

13. $\dfrac{N}{6}$ **14.** $w - 9$ **15.** $3m$ **16.** $4x + 45$ **17.** $\dfrac{w}{4}$ **18.** $n + 4$

Page 112   ***Exercise 2M***

1. $8a$ **2.** $4x$ **3.** $4a + 3b$ **4.** $6c - 4d$ **5.** $4d$ **6.** $3x + 2$
7. $9y$ **8.** $2h$ **9.** $3w$ **10.** y **11.** $7x + y$ **12.** $9m$
13. $7y$ **14.** $6m + 5n$ **15.** $4x + 6$ **16.** $13b$ **17.** $12t$ **18.** p
19. $25n$ **20.** $6a - 5$ **21.** $8x + 2$ **22.** $30h$ **23.** $9 - 7x$ **24.** $8b - 4$
25. $7a + 6$ **26.** $6c$ **27.** $12y - 12$ **28.** $11y$

Page 113   ***Exercise 2E***

1. $6a + 7b$ **2.** $9x + 7y$ **3.** $3x + 2y$ **4.** $3m + 8n$ **5.** $7a + 9$ **6.** $2a + 7b$
7. $3x + 2$ **8.** $9p + 5q$ **9.** $8x + 2$ **10.** $6a + 10b$ **11.** $12m + 1$ **12.** $2h + 25$
13. $12m + 6n$ **14.** $6p + 3q$ **15.** $9x + 4$ **16.** $8x + 3y + 6$ **17.** $4a + 3b + 4c$ **18.** $3w + 8$
19. $2a + 15$ **20.** $y + 3$ **21.** $6a + 12c$ **22.** $9p + 2q$ **23.** $7m + 2n + 4$ **24.** $14x + 8$
25. (a) $10x + 9$ (b) $12m + 11n + 6$ (c) $9a + 14b + 13$ **26.** (*b*) and (*c*)

Page 114   ***Exercise 3M***

1. (a) $xy = yx$, $x + y = y + x$ **2.** (a) $n + n = 2 \times n$, $n \times n = n^2$ **3.** true   **4.** true
5. false   **6.** true   **7.** false   **8.** true   **9.** false   **10.** false
11. false   **12.** false   **13.** true   **14.** false   **15.** (a) 1   (b) a
(c) n   (d) 6

Page 115   **Exercise 3E**

1. 8*ab*   **2.** 15*cd*   **3.** 42*mn*   **4.** 24*pq*   **5.** 18*ab*   **6.** 10*mnp*

7. 42*abc*   **8.** 24*pqr*   **9.** 30*ab*   **10.** (a) 12*xy*   (b) 12*wx*   (c) 8*mn*

11. (a) 2*pq*   (b) 7*xy* + 2*mn*   (c) 3*m* + 4*mn*   (d) 5*ab* + 2*a*   (e) *y* + 7*xy*   (f) 2*ab* + 13*cd* − 2*c*

  (g) *a* + 6*ab*   (h) *q* + 4 + 7*pq*   **12.** (a) 15*ac*   (b) 10*bc*   (c) 18*ac*   (d) 2*bc*

  (e) 12*bc*   (f) 18*ac* + 12*bc*   **13.** 2*ab*   **14.** 2*x* + *xy*

15. (12*a*, *b*), (*a*, 12*b*), (6*a*, 2*b*), (2*a*, 6*b*), (4*a*, 3*b*), (3*a*, 4*b*), (12*ab*, 1), (*ab*, 12), (6*ab*, 2), (2*ab*, 6), (4*ab*, 3), (3*ab*, 4)

Page 116   **Investigation – Number walls**

Part A: Largest total obtained by putting largest numbers in the middle of the base, smallest numbers at either end.

Part D: Pupils should be encouraged (and helped) to use algebra.
  With 3 bricks: Top brick = $a + 2b + c$
  With 4 bricks: Top brick = $a + 3b + 3c + d$
  With 5 bricks: Top brick = $a + 4b + 6c + 4d + e$

Pascal's triangle can be seen in the coefficients.

Page 118   **Exercise 4M**

1. 18   **2.** 37   **3.** £325   **4.** £47   **5.** 28   **6.** 58

7. (a) 50   (b) 122   (c) 43   **8.** 75

Page 118   **Exercise 4E**

1. 17   **2.** 15   **3.** 6   **4.** 32   **5.** 28   **6.** 9

7. 23   **8.** 14   **9.** 16   **10.** 50   **11.** 54   **12.** 80

13. 54   **14.** 55   **15.** 36   **16.** 5   **17.** 15   **18.** 4

19. 10   **20.** 108

Page 119   **Exercise 5M**

1. □ = 8   **2.** ○ = 5   **3.** ○ = 12   **4.** □ = 4   **5.** △ = 3   **6.** △ = 4

7. □ = 12   **8.** △ = 10   **9.** △ = 14   **10.** □ = 8   **11.** ○ = 9   **12.** ○ = 5

Page 119   **Exercise 5E**

1. □ = △ = 5   **2.** □ = 2, ○ = 4   **3.** ○ = $3\frac{1}{2}$ = △

4. △ = 3, ○ = 6   **5.** □ = △ = 4   **6.** △ = 3, ○ = 2

7. ○ = 2, □ = 4   **8.** △ = 10, □ = 5   **9.** ○ = 10, □ = 0

10. △ = 3, ○ = 0   **11.** △ = 3, ○ = 3   **12.** △ = 5, □ = 5

13. □ = 2, ○ = 6   **14.** □ = 4, △ = 8   **15.** △ = 4, ○ = 4

16. ◇ = 12

Page 122   ***Check Yourself on Section 2.5***

1. (a) $n - 6$ (b) $5x - 8$ (c) $2w + 24$ **2.** (a) $2m + 9n$ (b) $7y$ (c) $4p + 6$
   (d) $4xy + 4y$ **3.** (a) $28mn$ (b) $32pqr$ (c) C and D   **4.** (a) 645   (b) 6
   (c) 3   **5.** (a) $\square = 8$ (b) $\square = 12$, $\bigcirc = 3$

Page 123   ***Unit 2 Mixed Review***   ***Part one***

1. (a) $\dfrac{4}{5}$ (b) $\dfrac{1}{8}$ (c) $\dfrac{8}{15}$ **2.** isosceles   **3.** (a) $2x + 2y$ (b) $3n + 16$

5. (a) $5p + 6q$ (b) $2m + 2$ (c) $2xy + 8y$ **6.** (a) $15°$ (b) $40°$ (c) $35°$

   (d) $67°$ **7.** $\dfrac{9}{10}$ **8.** (a) $105°$ (b) $70°$ **9.** $\dfrac{17}{20}$ **10.** $55°$

11. 35, 36, 37, 38, 39   **12.** $23ab$ **13.** 5, 11   **14.** $74°$ **15.** 7.82
16. (a) 30   (b) 6   **17.** 3

Page 125   ***Part two***

1.

$\dfrac{4}{25}$	0.16	16%
$\dfrac{7}{10}$	0.7	70%
$\dfrac{3}{20}$	0.15	15%

2. $(4.9 \to 5)$ cm **3.** (b) AB = 4.5 cm   **4.** 44   **5.** (a) $2a + b + c$
   (b) $2a, a, 3a$ (c) $3m + n, 2m + 4n, 5m + 5n$ **6.** Sefton

7. (a) x = $68°$, y = $73°$ (b) $85°$ **8.** $\dfrac{1}{4}$ **9.** 0.57 or $\dfrac{57}{100}$ **10.** 11.4

11. 6   **12.** $90°$ **13.** $\dfrac{7}{8}$ **14.** $\dfrac{2}{n}$

15. (a) $6n + 3$ (b) C and D   (c) $4n$ (d) $13n + 8$
16. (a) possible   (b) false   (c) possible   **17.** $26°$ **18.** (a) 16   (b) 32.

Page 129   ***Puzzles and Problems 2***

Crossnumbers

Part A

¹5	4	²2		³1	5	1	⁴2
7		3		⁵5	6		1
	⁶4	5	⁷7	1		⁸9	6
⁹7	3		4		¹⁰3	1	
9		¹¹2	8	4		8	¹²5
9		5		¹³5	¹⁴8		8
¹⁵7	¹⁶2	6	8		¹⁷2	6	9
	1		¹⁸2	1	1		3

Part B

¹9	9	²0		³9	9	1	⁴0
2		2		⁵5	6		0
	⁶4	6	⁷8	4		⁸0	1
⁹8	6		2		¹⁰6	0	
2		¹¹8	0	8		3	¹²2
4		5		¹³9	¹⁴7		3
¹⁵2	¹⁶3	4	3		¹⁷3	5	3
	7		¹⁸2	2	5		1

Part C

[1] 1	6	[2] 9		[3] 5	2	0	[4] 0
8		2		[5] 2	1		6
	[6] 1	2	[7] 3	4		[8] 1	6
[9] 3	6		6		[10] 8	1	
6		[11] 7	2	0		0	[12] 2
0		5		[13] 1	[14] 6		3
[15] 0	[16] 2	3	4		[17] 0	0	4
	8		[18] 1	0	0		5

Part D

[1] 8	2	[2] 8		[3] 8	0	0	[4] 0
1		3		[5] 3	6		0
	[6] 1	2	[7] 1	0		[8] 8	4
[9] 2	4		0		[10] 6	6	
2		[11] 0	0	5		4	[12] 4
4		9		[13] 6	[14] 4		4
[15] 1	[16] 9	9	8		[17] 1	4	4
	0		[18] 3	7	1		4

Page 131   Mental Arithmetic Test 1

1. £9 each	**2.** 60%	**3.** 5	**4.** £1.66	**5.** 17012
6. 2250 mm	**7.** 110 min	**8.** 0.03	**9.** 282	**10.** £4.20
11. 420 km	**12.** 50, 5, 5, 1, 1 or 20, 20, 10, 10, 2		**13.** 5×9, 3×15, 1×45	
14. 13	**15.** 100 000	**16.** £8.97	**17.** £36	**18.** £3.35
19. 5.15	**20.** 24 cm	**21.** 60%	**22.** 15p	**23.** 16 days
24. 7	**25.** £100			

Page 132   Mental Arithmetic Test 2

1. 20, 10, 10, 2 or 20, 20, 1, 1	**2.** £3.02	**3.** 12 kg	**4.** 54	**5.** £1.88
6. 60°	**7.** 30	**8.** £11.05	**9.** 0.3 m	**10.** £5.25 **11.** 5%
12. 32%	**13.** 80	**14.** 50°	**15.** £80 000	**16.** 47 **17.** 26
18. 17	**19.** 10 000 cm²	**20.** Wednesday	**21.** True	**22.** 180 **23.** 3030
24. 81, 100, 121 etc.	**25.** 5.15			

Unit 3

*Page 134 **Exercise 1M***

1. C (4, 4)   D (1, 2)   E (7, 3)   F (3, 0)   G (2, 1)   H (0, 3)
I (6, 5)   **2.** (a) (4, 8)   (b) (7, 4)   (c) (6, 7)   (d) (3, 4)   (e) (8, 4)
(f) (5, 2)   **3.** (a) Hand grenade area   (b) Parachute drop zone   (c) Secret caves
(d) Hospital C   (e) Interrogation centre   (f) Helicopter pad   (g) Hospital B
(h) Look out point

*Page 135 **Exercise 1E***

¹P	A	²P	E	³R		⁴F	A	R
L		I		E		O		
⁵A	O	L		⁶A	U	R	A	L
S		O		D		M		
T		⁷T	R	I	B	U	T	E
E				N		L		
⁸R	E	⁹P	U	G	N	A	N	¹⁰T
E		A						A
¹¹D	E	R		¹²B	A	C	O	N

*Page 138 **Exercise 2E***

1. (a) (7, 7), (4, 6)   (b) (5, 11), (3, 10)   (c) (7, 3) (4, 2)
(d) (9, 0), (9, 2)   (e) (11, 7), $(10\frac{1}{2}, 9\frac{1}{2})$
2. (a) (1, 1)   (b) (6, 5)   (c) (6, 2)
3. (a) (4, 2)   (b) (8, 8)   (c) (3, 10)
4. P: (3, 6), (7, 2), (1, 2)   Q: (12, 4), (8, 6), (12, 12)   **5.** (a) (−4, 0)
(b) (1, 0)   (c) (3, 1)   (d) (2, 1)
6. (4, 3), (1, 5), (3, 1), (2, 7), (5, 6), (0, 2), (0, 4), (1, 4), (1, 6), (4, 2), (4, 4), (5, 4)
7. (a) (7, 3), (1, 5), (5, 1), (3, 7), (5, 3), (3, 5), (8, 0), (0, 8) etc
(b) Any points on the line $x + y = 8$
8. (d) (7, 5)   (f) (6, 6)   (g) (0, 1)

*Page 140 **Exercise 1M***

1. (a) 495   (b) 1075   (c) 666
2. (a) 1044   (b) 1134   (c) 7488   (d) 6624   (e) 729   (f) 7712
3. (b) remainder 2   **4.** 32   **5.** 34   **6.** 37
7. (a) 544   (b) 325   (c) 24   (d) 1210
8. £9.90   **9.** 65p   **10.** 759

Page 141   **Exercise 1E**

1. 22 r 3   **2.** 37 r 2   **3.** 42 r 7   **4.** 31 r 1   **5.** 32 r 19   **6.** 15 r 6
7. £43.68   **8.** 37   **9.** £13.95   **10.** 23 × 54   **11.** 13   **12.** 14, 24p over
13. £27   **14.** 37   **15.** 3306   **16.** 26 and 2 left over
17. No. We need 13 more chairs   **18.** £24 480

Page 143   **Exercise 1M**

1. 26.07   **2.** 14.3   **3.** 30.4   **4.** 1.74   **5.** 1.163   **6.** 12.61
7. 10.64   **8.** 3.14   **9.** 20   **10.** 1230   **11.** 194.5   **12.** 0.68
13. 3.92   **14.** 0.158   **15.** 0.006   **16.** 48.592
17. $8.2 + 4.8 = 13$ **18.** $7.2 \times 0.01 = 0.072$ **19.** $27.42 \div 3 = 9.14$
20. $11.14 - 3.64 = 7.5$ **21.** $90.2 \div 11 = 8.2$ **22.** $3.54 \times 7 = 24.78$
23. 75.48 cm²

Page 143   **Exercise IE**

1. ×   **2.** ÷   **3.** ×   **4.** ×   **5.** ×   **6.** ÷
7. 0.175 kg   **8.** £49.92   **9.** 12.58 cm   **10.** 138.7   **11.** 60.68 kg
12. (a) 7   (b) 4.2   **13.** 27.04 m²   **14.** 13   **15.** £5.40, £8.10
16. £111.50   **17.** £939.60   **18.** £255   **19.** 33.2 hours

Page 144   **Exercise 2M**

1. (a) F   (b) T   (c) F   (d) T   (e) F   (f) T
2. (a) 1.48, 0.148, 0.15, 150   (b) 1.05, 1.3, 0.26, 2.6
    (c) 1.7, 1.87, 2, 0.04
3.

¹3	²5	2		³6	⁴8
⁵8	1		⁶1	4	4
5		⁷4	9	0	
	⁸1	8			⁹4
¹⁰7	2	8		¹¹9	4
¹²1	0	1	2		1

Page 145   **Exercise 2E**

1.

57	÷	3	→	19
+		×		
147	+	53	→	200
↓		↓		
204	−	159	→	45

2.

18	×	5	→	90
×		+		
0.1	×	10	→	1
↓		↓		
1.8	+	15	→	16.8

3.

25	×	0.4	→	10
×		+		
6	×	0.6	→	3.6
↓		↓		
150	−	1	→	149

4.

35	×	100	→	3500
−		÷		
0.2	×	1000	→	200
↓		↓		
34.8	+	0.1	→	34.9

5.

48	×	9	→	432
÷		×		
16	×	13	→	208
↓		↓		
3	+	117	→	120

6.

5	−	0.2	→	4.8
÷		+		
100	−	2	→	98
↓		↓		
0.05	+	2.2	→	2.25

7.

10	×	0.2	→	2
÷		×		
4	÷	8	→	0.5
↓		↓		
2.5	−	1.6	→	0.9

8.

19.6	÷	7	→	2.8
×		−		
0.1	×	0.3	→	0.03
↓		↓		
1.96	+	6.7	→	8.66

9.

8.42	−	0.2	→	8.22
×		×		
15	×	80	→	1200
↓		↓		
126.3	+	16	→	142.3

10.

20	÷	100	→	0.2
×		÷		
22	×	200	→	4400
↓		↓		
440	×	0.5	→	220

11.

1.22	×	7	→	8.54
+		−		
3.78	+	3	→	6.78
↓		↓		
5	÷	4	→	1.25

12.

32.4	+	57.8	→	90.2
÷		−		
9	×	52	→	468
↓		↓		
3.6	×	5.8	→	20.88

Page 147 **Exercise 1M**

1. (a) 19　　　(b) 11　　　(c) 37
2. Prime numbers: 2, 3, 5, 7, 11, 13, 17, 19, 23, 29, 31, 37, 41, 43, 47, 53, 59, 61, 67, 71, 73, 79, 83, 89, 97
3. All the prime numbers in columns A and B can be written as the sum of two square numbers.
4. The pattern does continue.

Page 147 **Exercise 1E Part one**

1. (a) 17, 29　　(b) 41, 67　　(c) 2, 71　　　**2.** 25
3. 2 + 3 = 5, 2 + 5 = 7, 2 + 17 = 19 (many others)　**4.** One　　　**5.** 24
6. 3 and 7, 7 and 11, 13 and 17 (many others)　　**7.** 3 + 19, 5 + 17, 11 + 11
8. (a) 11, 31, 41, 61, 71 (+ others > 100)　　　(b) 7, 17, 37, 47, 67, 97　　　(c) Divisible by 5
9. True　　　**10.** 48 cm　　**11.** 3 + 5 + 11 = 19 (+ others)

Page 147 **Exercise 1E Part two**

1. 293, 709, 1009 are prime.
2. (a) 7 hours 12 minutes 42 seconds　　　　(b) 18 pages (17.3 actually)
3. (a) Yes　　(b) Yes　　(c) Yes　　(d) Yes
　(e) It appears to give a prime number every time but this is not a proof.

Page 149   ***Exercise 2M***

1. 1, 2, 3, 6   **2.** 1, 2, 4   **3.** 1, 2, 5, 10
4. 1, 7   **5.** 1, 3, 5, 15   **6.** 1, 2, 3, 6, 9, 18
7. 1, 2, 3, 4, 6, 8, 12, 24   **8.** 1, 3, 7, 21   **9.** 1, 2, 3, 4, 6, 9, 12, 18, 36
10. 1, 2, 4, 5, 8, 10, 20, 40   **11.** 1, 2, 4, 8, 16, 32   **12.** 1, 31
13. 1, 2, 3, 4, 5, 6, 10, 12, 15, 20, 30, 60   **14.** 1, 3, 7, 9, 21, 63
15. 1, 5, 17, 85   **16.** 6, 8   **17.** 18, 12
18. (a)   (b)

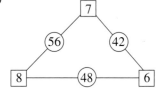   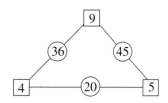

(c)   (d)

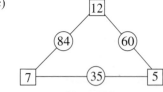   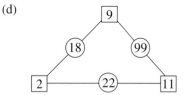

19. 4   **20.** (a) 6   (b) 16

Page 150   ***Exercise 2E***

1. (a) 1, 2, 5, 10, 25, 50   (b) 1, 2, 4, 11, 22, 44   (c) 1, 2, 4, 5, 10, 20, 25, 50, 100
      (d) 1, 29   **2.** (d) prime factors are $2 \times 2 \times 3 \times 3$
3. $2 \times 2 \times 7$ **4.** $2 \times 2 \times 2 \times 2 \times 2$ **5.** 2×17
6. $3 \times 3 \times 3 \times 3$ **7.** $2 \times 2 \times 3 \times 7$ **8.** $2 \times 2 \times 2 \times 3 \times 3 \times 3$
9. $2 \times 3 \times 7 \times 7$ **10.** $2 \times 2 \times 2 \times 5 \times 5$ **11.** $2 \times 2 \times 3 \times 5 \times 5 \times 5$
12. $2 \times 2 \times 2 \times 2 \times 2 \times 7 \times 11$ **13.** $2 \times 2 \times 3 \times 5 \times 7 \times 11$ **14.** $3 \times 5 \times 5 \times 7 \times 11 \times 17$
15. 5   **16.** (a) (i) d.s. = 6, factors = 8   (ii) d.s. = 12, factors = 12
17. 165 (+ others)   **18.** 198 (+ others)   **19.** 64 or 96
20. 210 ($2 \times 3 \times 5 \times 7$) + others   **21.** 2520 ($2^3 \times 3^2 \times 5 \times 7$)

Page 151   ***Exercise 3M***

1. 3, 6, 9, 12   **2.** 4, 8, 12, 16   **3.** 2, 4, 6, 8
4. 7, 14, 21, 28   **5.** 10, 20, 30, 40   **6.** 5, 10, 15, 20, 25, 30
7. 8, 16, 24, 32, 40, 48   **8.** 9, 18, 27, 36, 45, 54   **9.** 11, 22, 33, 44, 55, 66
10. 20, 40, 60, 80, 100, 120   **11.** (a) 5   (b) 7   (c) 2 and 4
12. 32   **13.** 101   **14.** 5   **15.** 56
16. 18   **17.** (a) 24, 60, 120   (b) 4, 6
18. (a) multiple   (b) factor   (c) factor   (d) factor
19. 12, 24, 36   **20.** 10, 20, 30   **21.** 30, 60, 90
22. 12 and 24 or 48 and 96

Page 152   *Exercise 3E*

1. (a) 2, 4, 6, 8, 10, 12   (b) 5, 10, 15, 20, 25, 30   (c) 10
2. (a) 4, 8, 12, 16   (b) 12, 24, 36, 48   (c) 12
3. (a) 3, 6, 9, 12, 15, 18   (b) 5, 10, 15, 20, 25, 30   (c) 15
4. (a) 18   (b) 24   (c) 70   (d) 12   (e) 30   (f) 252
5. 12   **6.** 6   **7.** (a) 6   (b) 11   (c) 9   (d) 6
    (e) 12   (f) 10   **8.** (a) 6   (b) 40   (c) 11, 22 (+ others)   (d) 2, 5
9. 15   **10.** 21   **11.** 66   **12.** 195

Page 154   *Exercise 4M*

2. (a) 25   (b) 64   (c) 100   (d) 1   **3.** (a) 25   (b) 14
    (c) 181   **4.** (a) $4 + 9$ (b) $9 + 64$ (c) $4 + 36$ (d) $81 + 100$ (e) $25 + 100$
    (f) $16 + 81$ (g) $25 + 49$ (h) $49 + 64$ **6.** (a) 64   (b) 81   (c) 169
7. $1 + 3 + 5 + 7 + 9 = 5^2$, $1 + 3 + 5 + 7 + 9 + 11 = 6^2$, $1 + 3 + 5 + 7 + 9 + 11 + 13 = 7^2$ etc

Page 154   *Exercise 4E*

1. 8   **2.** (a) 7   (b) 11   (c) 13
3. (a) 2, 4, 8, 16   (b) 2, 3, 7   (c) 3, 9, 15, 21   (d) 4, 9, 16, 64
4. (a) 16–9   (b) 81–1   (c) 100–16   (d) 400–100   (e) 49–4
    (f) 36–4   (g) 64–25   (h) 121–16   **5.** (a) 5   (b) 9
    (c) 7   (d) 1   **6.** (a) 7   (b) 14   (c) $\sqrt{441} = 21$
    (d) $\sqrt{10.89} = 3.3$ **7.** (a) $1 + 9$ (b) $16 + 4 + 4$ (c) $36 + 9 + 1 + 1$
    (d) $64 + 1 + 1$ (e) $81 + 16 + 1$ (f) $49 + 9 + 4 + 1$ (g) $100 + 16 + 4$
    (h) $121 + 16 + 4$ (i) $225 + 196 + 1 + 1$ **8.** $4^3 = 64$, $5^3 = 125$, $6^3 = 216$
9. 8, 64, 1000   **10.** $13 + 15 + 17 + 19 = 64 = 4^3$ $21 + 23 + 25 + 27 + 29 = 125 = 5^3$
    $31 + 33 + 35 + 37 + 39 + 41 = 216 = 6^3$ **11.** 3   **12.** 5

Page 156   *Satisfied Numbers* [Other solutions are possible]

1.

	Number between 5 and 9	Square number	Prime number
Factor of 6	6	1	3
Even number	8	4	2
Odd number	7	9	5

2.

	Prime number	Multiple of 3	Factor of 16
Number greater than 5	7	9	8
Odd number	5	3	1
Even number	2	6	4

3. Many solutions

Page 157   **Happy numbers**

The Happy numbers are:- 1, 7, 10, 13, 19, 23, 28, 31, 32, 44, 49, 68, 70, 79, 82, 86, 91, 94, 97, 100
Encourage pupils to find 'short cuts'. E.g. if 23 is happy, so is 32.

Page 158   **Check Yourself on Units 3.1, 3.2, 3.3 and 3.4**

1. (a) (5, 3)   (b) (7, 5)   (c) (4, 3)
2. (a) 945   (b) 17 658   (c) 45   (d) 11
3. (a) 12.24, 13, 2.6   (b) £11.75   (c) 7 cm
4. (a) (i) 3, 31   (ii) 3, 51   (iii) 4, 8   (b) 3 + 97, 11 + 89 (+ others)
5. (a) 24   (b) 15   (c) 108
      (d) (i) 9   (ii) 189   (iii) 10   (e) 3, 4, 5

Page 160   **Exercise 1M**

1. A: $y = 7$, B: $y = 3$, C: $y = 1\frac{1}{2}$ **2.** P: $x = 5$, Q: $x = 3$, R: $x = -3$

3. A: $x = 3$, B: $y = 2$, C: $y = -2$ **4.** A: $y = 2$, B: $x = 4$, C: $x = -2$
5. (a) (3, 2)   (b) (1, 5)   (c) (7, 3)
6. (a) $x = 1$ (b) $y = 7$ (c) $x = 2$ (d) $x = 7$
      (e) $x = 3$ (f) $y = 3$ (g) $y = 5$ (h) $y = 0$

Page 162   **Exercise 1E**

1. (1, 3), (2, 4) (3, 5) etc. $y = x + 2$ **2.** (1, 0), (2, 1), (3, 2) etc, $y = x - 1$
3. $y = x + 4$ **4.** $x + y = 6$ (or $y = 6 - x$)   **5.** $x + y = 4$
6. $y = 2x$ **7.** (a) $y = 2x + 1$ (b) $y = 2x - 4$

   (c) $y = 11$ (d) $y = x - 5$ **8.** $y = \dfrac{1}{2}x + 8$

9. $y = 3x - 27$ **10.** $x + y = 7$ (or $y = 7 - x$)

Page 163   **Exercise 2M**

1. (a) 7   (b) 9   (c) 4   **2.** (a) 3   (b) 5   (c) 7
3. (a) 6   (b) 15   (c) 0   **4.** A and C   **5.** B and C
6. $y = x - 2$: C; $y = 8 - x$: A; $x = 4$ not marked; $y = 4$: D; $y = 2x$: B
7. A: $y = x + 2$,   B: $y = 2x$,   C: $y = 2x$,   D: $y = 2x$,   E: $y = x + 2$,   F: $y = x + 2$
8. P, S and T are on $y = 3x - 2$; Q, R and U are on $y = x - 3$

Page 164   **Exercise 2E**

1. (2, 5) (3, 6) (4, 7)   **2.** (2, 7) (3, 8) (4, 9)   **3.** (2, 0) (3, 1) (4, 2)
4. (2, –2) (3, –1) (4, 0)   **5.** (2, 4) (3, 6) (4, 8)   **6.** (0, 1) (2, 5) (4, 9)
7. (0, –2) (2, 2) (4, 6)   **8.** (1, 5) (3, 3) (5, 1) (6, 0)   **9.** (0, 4) (2, 2) (4, 0)
10. (0, 2) (1, 5) (2, 8)   **11.** (2, 3)   **12.** (c) (0, 3) (6, 9) (8, 7)

Page 165   *Exercise 1M*

1. (a) football   (b) 5   (c) 25   **2.** (a) 5   (b) 30
4. (a) 8   (b) £3.50
5. (a) 30 cm   (b) June   (c) December   (d) April, May, July, September
(e) February, March, August, October

Page 167   *Exercise 1E*

1. (a) C   (b) D   (c) B   (d) A
2. (a) 40   (b) 10   (c) 40   (d) Belair
3. (a) 60% loss of farming land   (b) golf, walking, sports
(c) loss of farming land used now for residential buildings
4. Wheat production has increased from 4 million tonnes to 14 million tonnes
Rice production has not changed
Sugar cane has increased to 2 million tonnes
Cotton seed has increased to 3 million tonnes.
5. (a) Former Commonwealth countries make up for the difference, plus U.S.A.
6. Tallies in order: E = 10, M = 10, F = 4, N = 15, S = 6

Page 170   *Exercise 2M*

1. (a) Frequencies: 1, 4, 3, 5, 7   (b) 12   **2.** (a) Frequencies: 2, 4, 8, 8
3. (c) This time we have children and adults. In question 2 we had only children.
4. (a) 7   (b) 7   (c) 19
5. Pigs' weight has increased on high fibre diet   **6.** Yes. The pills did help to improve memory

Page 172   *Exercise 2E*

1. Theory was not correct. Those who watched most T.V. did *better* in the tests than they did before.
The results of the other group were neither better nor worse than before.
2. (a) 30 litres   (b) 15.00   (c) 20 litres
(d) fuel tank was filled   (e) car was stationary   (f) 60 litres
3. (a) Warm and dry   (b) Wednesday
(c) Both days had little rain but higher temperature on Saturday
4. (a) 10   (b) 24   (c) 34
5. (a) 4/5%   (b) 11%   (c) (i) 4/5%   (ii) 0.5%
(d) Far more old people in U.K. (Better health care, diet etc.)
(e) Kenya half male, half female. Saudi Arabia significantly more males

Page 174   *Exercise 3M*

1. (a) $\frac{1}{2}$ (b) $\frac{1}{4}$ (c) 100 g   **2.** (a) $\frac{1}{4}$ (b) $\frac{1}{8}$ (c) 10

3. 1208   **4.**

Method	car	walk	train	bus
Number of people	40	10	20	10

5. (a) USA   (b) Greece or USA   (c) 25   **6.** (a) 50   (b) 75
7. (a) 8 boys chose red, 5 girls chose red, John is wrong   (b) 10 boys chose blue, Tara is right

Page 176   **Exercise 3E**

1. (a) £6.00   (b) £6.00   (c) £3.00   (d) £4.00   (e) £3.00   (f) £2.00
2. (a) (i) 120   (ii) 135   (b) 18°   (c) 30
3. (a) 36 g   (b) 1 g = 10°   (c) Oats 60°, Barley 90°, Sugar 30°, Rye 180°

4. Programme	Angle		**5.** Sport	Angle		**6.** Subject	Angle
News	40°		Rugby	75°		Maths	45°
Soap	100°		Football	105°		English	45°
Comedy	80°		Tennis	60°		Science	54°
Drama	100°		Squash	30°		Humanities	36°
Film	40°		Athletics	45°		Arts	36°
			Swimming	45°		Other	144°

7. 1 meal = 3°   **8.** (a) $\dfrac{1}{3}$ (b) 30 children   (c) 18 children

10. (a) 15%   (b) $x = 126°$ $y = 109°$
11. (a) 5 → 10%   (b) About 150   (c) There were more people on the ferry

Page 180   **Exercise 1M and 1E**

For discussion

Page 183   **Exercise 3M**

1. $\dfrac{3}{4}$ **2.** $\dfrac{1}{4}$ **3.** $\dfrac{1}{2}$ **4.** 0   **5.** $\dfrac{3}{5}$ **6.** $\dfrac{1}{3}$

7. 1   **8.** $\dfrac{11}{12}$ **9.** (a) $\dfrac{1}{2}$ (b) $\dfrac{1}{2}$ (c) $\dfrac{1}{6}$ (d) $\dfrac{1}{8}$

11. $\dfrac{1}{7}$ **12.** (a) $\dfrac{1}{3}$ (b) $\dfrac{1}{3}$ (c) $\dfrac{1}{3}$ **13.** (a) $\dfrac{1}{4}$ (b) $\dfrac{1}{4}$

(c) $\dfrac{1}{4}$ (d) $\dfrac{1}{8}$ **14.** (a) $\dfrac{1}{2}$ (b) $\dfrac{1}{2}$ (c) 0

Page 185   **Exercise 3E**

1. (a) $\dfrac{1}{5}$ (b) $\dfrac{1}{5}$ (c) 0   **2.** (a) $\dfrac{2}{3}$ (b) $\dfrac{1}{3}$

3. (a) $\dfrac{1}{3}$ (b) $\dfrac{2}{3}$ **4.** (a) $\dfrac{6}{11}$ (b) $\dfrac{3}{11}$ (c) $\dfrac{1}{11}$ (d) $\dfrac{10}{11}$

5. (a) $\dfrac{1}{9}$ (b) $\dfrac{1}{3}$ (c) $\dfrac{4}{9}$ **6.** (a) $\dfrac{1}{6}$ (b) $\dfrac{1}{6}$ (c) $\dfrac{2}{3}$

7. (a) $\dfrac{1}{8}$ (b) $\dfrac{1}{2}$ (c) $\dfrac{5}{8}$ **8.** (a) $\dfrac{1}{9}$ (b) $\dfrac{1}{3}$ (c) $\dfrac{5}{9}$

9. (a) $\dfrac{7}{12}$ (b) $\dfrac{1}{6}$ (c) $\dfrac{5}{12}$

(d) $\dfrac{7}{12}$ $\left[\text{or} \dfrac{3}{4} \text{ if Pinahas eat sharks}\right]$ (e) 0 (unless it is a tuna)

10. (a) $\dfrac{4}{11}$ (b) $\dfrac{7}{11}$ **11.** (a) $\dfrac{2}{11}$ (b) $\dfrac{4}{11}$ (c) $\dfrac{7}{11}$ **12.** (a) $\dfrac{1}{8}$

(b) $\dfrac{1}{8}$ (c) $\dfrac{1}{4}$ (d) $\dfrac{1}{2}$ **13.** (a) $\dfrac{1}{10}$ (b) $\dfrac{3}{25}$ (c) $\dfrac{3}{10}$

(d) $\dfrac{1}{10}$ (e) $\dfrac{3}{50}$ (f) $\dfrac{1}{50}$ **14.** (a) $\dfrac{1}{4}$ (b) $\dfrac{3}{8}$ (c) $\dfrac{1}{2}$

(d) $\dfrac{1}{8}$ (e) $\dfrac{7}{8}$ **15.** (a) $\dfrac{5}{26}$ (b) $\dfrac{1}{26}$ (c) $\dfrac{3}{26}$ (d) $\dfrac{5}{26}$

Page 187   **Check Yourself on Units 3.5, 3.6 and 3.7**

1. (a) (1, 4)   (b) $x = 1$ (c) $y = 2$ (d) (3, 3)   **2.** (a) $y = x - 2$
   (b) (i) $y = x + 3$ (ii) $y = 2x$ (c) P, R   (d) 1, 3, 5
3. (b) AB no rain, no use;   BC rainfall;   CD no use;   DE water used;   EF no use;   FG rainfall;
    GH no use;
4. (a) 175   (b) 300   (c) 200

5. (a) (i) $\dfrac{1}{4}$ (ii) $\dfrac{5}{8}$ (iii) $\dfrac{3}{8}$ (iv) $\dfrac{1}{3}$ (b) (i) $\dfrac{1}{52}$ (ii) $\dfrac{1}{13}$

   (iii) $\dfrac{1}{2}$ **6.** (a) white   (b) (i) $\dfrac{7}{11}$ (ii) $\dfrac{3}{11}$ (iii) 0   (iv) $\dfrac{1}{11}$

Page 189   **Exercise 1M**

1. £489.40   **2.** 13:50   **3.** 1476   **5.** £5.30   **6.** £93.12   **7.** 6 012 011
8. (a) 25 cm²   (b) 80 cm   **9.** 34 and 4 left over   **10.** (a) 90 mm   (b) 9.0 cm

Page 190   **Exercise 2M**

1. (a) 17   (b) 22   (c) 1.5   (d) 200
3. 0.08 mm   **4.** £300 000 000.00
5. (a) 2010 shekels   (b) Rome
6. (b) 80%   **7.** (a) 36   (b) 11, 17   (c) 16, 36
9. (a) 37   (b) 4 cm   **10.** 84

2.

11	8	5	10
2	13	16	3
14	1	4	15
7	12	9	6

Page 191   Exercise 3M

1. (a) 575 + 326   (b) 369 + 584 = 953   (c) 216 + 534   **2.** 10

3. (a) 23   (b) 31   (c) 55   **4.** 438   **5.** 5   **6.** 3784

7. 50, 5, 2;   50, 2, 2, 2, 1;   50, 5, 1, 1;   50, 2, 2, 1, 1, 1;   20, 20, 10, 5, 2;   20, 20, 10, 5, 1, 1;

20, 10, 10, 10, 5, 2;   20, 20, 5, 5, 5, 2   **8.** 47 days   **9.** (a) 564   (b) 527   (c) 68

(d) 4695   (e) 32.05   (f) 6432   **10.** 20

Page 193   Exercise 4M

1. £1928   **2.** 5, 13   **3.** 355   **4.** 0.03, 0.2, 0.201, 0.32, 0.4

5. Just over 596 years   **6.** £10.23   **7.** 6561   **8.** (a) 574 + 322 + 147 = 1043

(b) 2324 + 3502 + 2315 = 8141   **9.** 189 years   **10.** 23

Page 194   Exercise 5M

1. (a) $\dfrac{6+6}{6}$ (b) 7 + 7 − 7   (c) $\dfrac{99}{9}$ (d) $4+4+\dfrac{4}{4}$ (e) $\dfrac{4+4+4}{4}$

2. (a) 20   (b) 1008 mm   **3.**   **4.** 440 g   **5.** 5 250 000

6. (a) 1014 mm   (b) 101.4 cm   (c) more than 1m   **7.** 54 × 3 = 162

8. 72%   **9.** 64 g   **10.** (a) 14   (b) 32, 95   (c) 3, 8, 23

Page 195   Exercise 6M

1. (a) £24 000 000   (b) €12 000 000   **2.** 8 km   **3.** (a) 13.6 g   (b) 50 p   **4.** £625.50

5. 225 litres   **6.** (a) 288   (b) $\dfrac{1}{66}$ **7.** 25   **8.** £26.10

9. (a) 3, 16   (b) 12, 15   **10.** four   **11.** 50.86 m   **12.** 15

Page 196   Number Rings

Multiples of 13 do not form number rings. For example 13, 26, 39 etc.

Page 197   Unit 3 Mixed Review   Part one

1. (a) 7.1   (b) 100   (c) 10   (d) 1000   (e) 100   (f) 100

2. (a) What do you call a man with a spade in his head? Doug   (b) without, Douglas

(c) What do you call a dead parrot? Polygon

3. (a) $x = 2$ (b) $y = 4$ (c) $y = x$ **4.** (a) 4, 8, 12, 16, 20   (b) 1, 2, 3, 4, 6, 12

(c) 2, 3   **5.** (a) $\dfrac{1}{6}$ (b) $\dfrac{5}{6}$ **6.** £27   **7.** (a) 3.27 + 1.74 = 5.01

(b) 4.55 + 0.63 = 5.18   (c) 3.64 − 1.57 = 2.07   **8.** 57.6 tonnes

9. (a) 96   (b) 121   **10.** (a) 0.605, 0.65, 0.7, 0.702, 0.71

(b) 0.079, 0.08, 0.1, 0.99   (c) 0.007×10^2, 1^3, (2×3), 2^3, 3^2 **11.** (2, 0) (3, 1) (4, 2)
12. (a) 10   (b) 16   (c) 8   (d) 2   **13.** (a) 55 p   (b) £2.25
14. €142.50   **15.** (a) 12.8, 128, 125.1   (b) 100, 5.8, 0.58   (c) 2.55, 3, 3000

Part two

1. (a) 16   (b) 20   (c) 14   **2.** (a) 231   (b) 225   **3.** 6110 seconds
4. (a) £668   **5.** (a) 4, 8, 12, 16, 20, 24, 28   (b) 7, 14, 21, 28, 35, 42   (c) 28
6. (a) Stationary   (b) Filled up   (c) Half a tank   (d) 1800

7. $8085   **8.** 0.067 mm (3 d.p.)   **9.** 4, 8, 12, 12, 4   **10.** $\dfrac{1}{3}$

11. (a) $3.25 + 1.75 = 5$ (b) $100 \times 0.037 = 3.7$ (c) $2.73 - 0.23 = 2.5$ (d) $(1.3 + 1.2) \times 10 = 25$
12. £8.30   **13.** 504   **14.** (a) $x = 2$ (b) $x = 1$
15. (a) T   (b) T   (c) F   (d) F   (e) T

Page 202   Puzzles and Problems 3

1. (a)   (b)   (c)

(d) 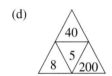   (e) 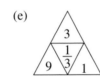   (f)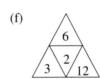

2. $\boxed{9} - \boxed{5} = \boxed{4}$ **3.** (a) $4 \times 4 - 4 = 12$ (b) $8 \div 8 + 8 = 9$ (c) $8 \times 8 + 8 = 72$
$\boxed{6} \div \boxed{3} = \boxed{2}$ **4.** (a) +   (b) ÷   (c) ×   (d) ÷   (e) −
$\boxed{1} + \boxed{7} = \boxed{8}$ **5.** (a) +   (b) −, −   (c) +

6. 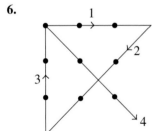   **7.**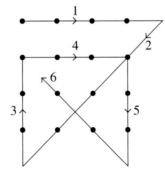

8. (a) M = 2, E = 1, A = 4 or M = 4, E = 2, A = 8
   (b) K = 1, L = 8, M = 5
   (c) E = 0, V = 5, A = 3, S = 8; N, W, R = 1, 2, 4 in any order
9. (a) many solutions   (b) many solutions   (c) S = 1, O = 3, N = 9, U = 4, W = 0, I = 2

(d) 1 2 4 5   or   2 3 4 5   (e) 2 9 8 0
      3 2 4 5   1 3 4 5   2 1 7 6 +
      5 2 6 5 +   5 3 6 5 +   5 1 5 6
      9 7 5 5   9 0 5 5

Page 204   **Mental Arithmetic Test 1**

1. 1500   **2.** £272   **3.** £600   **4.** 70°   **5.** £5   **6.** 210
7. 8 cm   **8.** 1945   **9.** 495 mm   **10.** 295 cm   **11.** five-to-seven
12. 3300 g   **13.** 102.5   **14.** 135 miles   **15.** $1\frac{1}{2}$ **16.** 47
17. 50p, 10p, 2p, 2p, 2p or 20p, 20p, 20p, 5p, 1p (there are other ways)
18. 45 litres   **19.** 19 hours   **20.** 10000   **21.** 80   **22.** −2
23. £10 million   **24.** 221   **25.** 5%

Page 204   **Mental Arithmetic Test 2**

1. £26   **2.** 1020   **3.** 24 cm²   **4.** 25   **5.** 2.85
6. 11   **7.** 1.65 m   **8.** 0.09   **9.** 0.25   **10.** 0.36
11. 2   **12.** 55   **13.** 7990   **14.** 23   **15.** $\frac{1}{8}$
16. 150 m   **17.** 3 500 000   **18.** 120 000   **19.** 15 cm or 0.15 m   **20.** 37
21. 1081   **22.** 84 cm   **23.** 250   **24.** £525   **25.** 120°

Page 206   **A long time ago! 3**

Exercise

1. £7 9s. 4d.   **2.** £10 6s. 11d.   **3.** £13 11s. 2d.   **4.** £15 18s. 7d.   **5.** £21 8s. 2d.
6. £74 8s. 4d.   **7.** 48   **8.** 42   **9.** 5s. 6d.   **10.** 4d.   **11.** 6d.

Unit 4

Page 207 **Exercise 1M**

1. (a) 40 (b) 110° (c) 55° **2.** 7.0 cm **3.** 7.0 cm **4.** 7.4 cm
5. 15.0 cm **6.** 9.4 cm **7.** 11.3 cm **8.** 8.7 cm **9.** 10.3 cm

Page 208 **Exercise 1E**

1. $m = 60°$, $n = 120°$ **2.** $x = 115°$, $y = 65°$ **3.** 5.9 cm **4.** 10.8 cm
5. 14.1 cm **6.** 50°

Page 209 **Exercise 2M**

1. 57° **2.** 29° **3.** 84° **4.** 103° **5.** 40° **6.** 40° **7.** 49°

Page 210 **Exercise 2E**

1. 98° **2.** 64° **3.** 50° **4.** 164° to 165° **5.** £389 000

Page 212 **Exercise 1M**

1. (a) trapezium (b) kite (c) regular hexagon (d) square
(e) rectangle (f) equilateral triangle (g) heptagon (h) regular pentagon
(i) rhombus (j) regular decagon (k) trapezium (l) pentagon
(m) isosceles triangle (n) quadrilateral (o) parallelogram (p) regular octagon
(q) hexagon (r) trapezium (s) rectangle (t) parallelogram
2. B **3.** diagonals are perpendicular, diagonals bisect each other
4. A–square, B–rhombus, C–kite, D–parallelogram, E–trapezium, F–rectangle

Page 214 **Exercise 1E**

1. none **2.** **3.** rectangle, rhombus **4.** 2

5. square **6.** **7.** 3 **8.** 2
9. parallelogram, rectangle, rhombus **10.** kite, trapezium

Page 215 **Investigation triangles and quadrilaterals**

1. Eight different triangles:

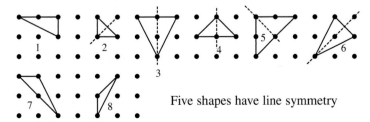

Five shapes have line symmetry

2. Sixteen different quadrilaterals:

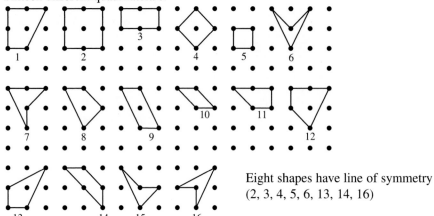

Eight shapes have line of symmetry
(2, 3, 4, 5, 6, 13, 14, 16)

Page 215 **Check Yourself on Sections 4.1 and 4.2**

1. (a) 70°　　　　　(b) 5.3 cm or 5.4 cm　　**2.** (a) 43°　　　　(b) 49°　　　　　　**3.** (a) trapezium

(b) square　　　　(c) rhombus　　　　　(d) kite　　　　　(e) parallelogram

(f) Four equal sides, opposite sides are parallel, opposite angles are equal, two lines of symmetry, rotational symmetry order 2, diagonals perpendicular to each other, diagonals bisect each other.

4. (a) P, R　　　　　(b) 10　　　　　　(c) This shape is a regular octagon　　　　**5.** (a) 2　(b) 1

(c) The diagonal line of symmetry does not allow one half of the rectangle to fold exactly onto the other half of the rectangle.

Page 217 **Exercise 1M**

1. (a) $\frac{3}{5} = \frac{6}{10} = 0.6$　　　　　　(b) $\frac{11}{20} = \frac{55}{100} = 0.55$　　　　　(c) $0.9 = \frac{9}{10} = \frac{90}{100} = 90\%$

(d) $0.17 = \frac{17}{100} = 17\%$　　**2.** $\frac{1}{20}$　　**3.** (a) 0.37　　(b) 0.6　　(c) 0.06　　(d) 0.19　　(e) 0.45

4. (a) False　　　　　(b) True　　(c) True　　　(d) False　　(e) True　　(f) False

5. (a) $\frac{4}{5}$　　　　　　(b) $\frac{47}{100}$　　(c) $\frac{4}{25}$　　　(d) $\frac{17}{20}$　　(e) $\frac{3}{4}$

6.

$\frac{7}{10}$	0.7	70%
$\frac{6}{25}$	0.24	24%
$\frac{23}{50}$	0.46	46%
$\frac{19}{20}$	0.95	95%
$\frac{3}{20}$	0.15	15%

Page 218   ***Exercise 1E***

1. (a) 0.34   (b) 0.76   (c) 0.65   (d) 0.45

2. (a) $\frac{7}{10}$, $\frac{3}{4}$, 0.8   (b) $\frac{11}{20}$, 0.57, 60%   (c) $\frac{1}{5}$, 24%, $\frac{1}{4}$ (d) 0.8, 82%, $\frac{21}{25}$

3. (a) $\frac{3}{4}$ (b) 75%   **4.** $\frac{64}{100}$, $\frac{128}{200}$, $\frac{16}{25}$

5. (a) $\frac{49}{100}$ (b) $\frac{2}{25}$ (c) $\frac{14}{25}$ (d) $\frac{3}{20}$

6. $\frac{17}{20}$, 0.85, 85%; $\frac{4}{5}$, 0.8, 80%; $\frac{1}{4}$, 0.25, 25%, $\frac{3}{25}$, 0.12, 12%; $\frac{22}{25}$, 0.88, 88%

Page 219   ***Exercise 2M***

1. 44%   **2.** 35%   **3.** 17%   **4.** 36%   **5.** 70%   **6.** 40%

7. D(25%), A(28%), C(30%), B(65%)   **8.** 25%   **9.** 10 080

Page 220   ***Exercise 2E***

1. 55%   **2.** 31%   **3.** $66\frac{2}{3}$%   **4.** (a) 10%   (b) 20%   **5.** 44%

6. (a) 38%   (b) 7%   (c) 18%   **7.** 22%   **8.** 24%

Page 222   ***Exercise 3M***

1. (a) £15   (b) £18   (c) £7   (d) £14   (e) £27   (f) £20

2. 36   **3.** 132   **4.** (a) £160   (b) £22   (c) £280   (d) £12

(e) £4   (f) £12   **5.** 25% of £60   **6.** same   **7.** (b)   **8.** £46

9. (a) £42   (b) £15   (c) £560   (d) £4   (e) £24   (f) £58 900

10. 57 kg   **11.** 448   **12.** (a) £1400   (b) £38.50   (c) £13.30   **13.** £846

14. 475 g

Page 224   ***Exercise 3E***

1. (a) £3.75   (b) £3.70   (c) £0.49   (d) £1.80   **2.** (a) £36.80

(b) £20.70   (c) £76.80   (d) £2774   (e) £96.90   (f) £1128

3. 9% of £21   **4.** (a) 2190 kg   (b) 74.2 km   (c) $7.05   (d) 14.62 km

(e) 282 m   (f) 6958 g   **5.** £224   **6.** (a) £1.14   (b) £2.98

(c) £6.27   (d) £0.57   (e) £418.76   (f) £0.93   **7.** (a) £213.90

(b) £697.50   (c) £437.10   (d) £799.80   **8.** £239.20   **9.** 84.8 kg

10. (a) £81.20   (b) £186.20   (c) £201.60   (d) £4469   **11.** £182.40

12. 2.94 kg   **13.** 1.7874 m   **14.** £362.10   **15.** £202 207.50   **16.** (a) 559

(b) 172

Page 226   ***Exercise 1M***

1. (a) $\frac{1}{4}$ (b) $\frac{3}{8}$ **2.** $\frac{1}{4}$ **4.** 60%   **5.** 120 g   **6.** £1.71

7. £770   **8.** £75   **9.** £294   **10.** 400

Page 226 **Exercise 1E**

1. £18 **2.** £108 **3.** 165 minutes **4.** 16 **5.** 41.6 litres **6.** 10

7. (a) 180 (b) 9 (c) 10 (d) 6 **8.** 6000 **9.** 96 minutes **10.** $\dfrac{nb}{b+5}$

Page 227 **Exercise 2M**

1. (a) 1:2 (b) 5:3 **2.** 11:16 **3.** 5:3 **5.** 19:14 **6.** (a) 1:4 (b) 4:5
  (c) 1:11 (d) 4:3 (e) 5:4:3 (f) 3:5 (g) 13:5 (h) 2:3:8 **7.** (a) 4
  (b) 3 (c) 7 (d) 15 (e) 3 (f) 4 **8.** 3:4:6

Page 229 **Exercise 2E**

1. (a) £27 : £9 (b) £6 : £30 (c) £24 : £12 **2.** (a) £30 : £45 (b) £33 : £42 (c) £40 : £35
3. (a) 16 (b) 12 **4.** 27 **5.** 81 **6.** £40 **7.** 63
8. £10 **9.** 12 **10.** (a) 12 Litres (b) 7:5 **11.** 30 hours
12. $\dfrac{1}{5}$ **13.** Rob £11500, Louise £17000, Steve £6500, Gemma £5000 **14.** 264 kg

Page 230 **Check Yourself on Sections 4.3 and 4.4**

1.

(a)	$\dfrac{2}{25}$	0.08	8%
(b)	$\dfrac{4}{5}$	0.8	80%
(c)	$\dfrac{9}{10}$	0.9	90%
(d)	$\dfrac{8}{25}$	0.32	32%
(e)	$\dfrac{18}{25}$	0.72	72%

2. (a) 40% (b) maths test **3.** (a) £18 (b) £285

  (c) £96 (d) £0.72 **4.** (a) $\dfrac{13}{22}$ (b) £61.32

5. (a) 3:8 (b) 9 (c) £80

Page 232 **Exercise 1M**

1. (a) −6 (b) −6 (c) −8 (d) −13 (e) 2 (f) 4
  (g) −11 (h) −4 (i) 0 (j) −9 (k) −7 (l) −12
2. (a) 9 (b) 0 (c) −7 (d) −9 (e) 0 (f) −12
  (g) 1 (h) −2 (i) −30 (j) −20 (k) −40 (l) −4
3. −8 **4.** (a) 4 (b) 11 (c) −5 (d) −3 (e) −9
  (f) −11 (g) −2 (h) 10 (i) 16 (j) −12 (k) 0
  (l) −11

5. (a)

```
        0
     1    -1
  -1    2    -3
-4    3    -1    -2
```

(b)

```
            -35
        -17    -18
     -3    -14    -4
   4    -7    -7    3
 6    -2    -5    -2    5
```

(c)

```
             5
         2       3
      -2    4    -1
   -5    3    1    -2
 -3   -2   5   -4    2
```

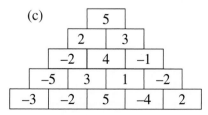

6. (a) 1   (b) –6   (c) 1   (d) 0   (e) –4   (f) –3
    (g) –1   (h) 0   (i) –12   (j) –7   (k) 1   (l) –7
7. (a) 4   (b) 10   (c) –2   (d) –4   (e) –2   (f) –9

8. (a)

3	2	–2
–4	1	6
4	0	–1

(b)

0	1	–4
–5	–1	3
2	–3	–2

9. (a) true   (b) false   (c) true   (d) true   (e) false
    (f) false   (g) true   (h) false   (i) false

Page 234   **Exercise 1E**

1. (a) –8   (b) –20   (c) –12   (d) 6   (e) –18   (f) –16
    (g) 30   (h) –7   **2.** (a) –4   (b) –5   (c) –4   (d) 3
    (e) 3   (f) –5   (g) –5   (h) 3   **3.** (a) –2   (b) –48
    (c) 28   (d) –32   (e) 2   (f) –3   (g) –90   (h) 9
4. –8, – 1;   –4, – 2

5. (a)

×	–4	–7	2	0	–8	5
3	–12	–21	6	0	–24	15
–9	36	63	–18	0	72	–45
6	–24	–42	12	0	–48	30
–4	16	28	–8	0	32	–20
–6	24	42	–12	0	48	–30
–1	4	7	–2	0	8	–5

(b)

×	–3	7	10	–4	–6
–2	6	–14	–20	8	12
4	–12	28	40	–16	–24
–5	15	–35	–50	20	30
8	–24	56	80	–32	–48
–3	9	–21	–30	12	18

6. (a) –8   (b) 30   (c) 9   (d) 36   (e) –32   (f) –40
    (g) 1   (h) –8   **7.** (a) 7   (b) –7   (c) –2   (d) –9
    (e) –50   (f) 72   (g) –12   (h) –15   (i) –21

Page 235   **Exercise 1M**

1. $2w - 18$ **2.** $2p + q + 8$ **3.** (a) $3y$ (b) $8m + 2$ (c) $6x$ (d) $5w - 3$
4. $2n + n, 3n$ **5.** (a) 2   (b) w **6.** 34   **7.** $w = 5$ **8.** $a = 8$
9. $p = 47$ **10.** $a = 80$ **11.** $y = 3$ **12.** $m = 185$

Page 236 **Exercise 1E**

1. $\dfrac{x}{9} - 14$ **2.** $n - y - 3$ **3.** (a) $2m + 9n$ (b) $13y + 2w$

(c) $x + 7$ (d) $9a + 3b + 3$ **4.** (a) $8mn$ (b) $15wyz$ (c) $72pqr$ **5.** $34mn$

6. (a) $3mn$ (b) $xy + 7x$ (c) $7pq$ (d) $a + 9 + 7ab$ **7.** $w = 19$ **8.** $h = -24$

9. $n = -10$ **10.** $p = 36$ **11.** $y = 30$ **12.** $p = -10$ **13.** $a = -18$ **14.** $y = -21$

15. $p = 34$ **16.** $m = 61$

Page 237 **Exercise 2M**

1. 8	**2.** 12	**3.** 20	**4.** 6	**5.** 9	**6.** 7
7. 5	**8.** 8	**9.** 6	**10.** 4	**11.** 9	**12.** 8

Page 239 **Exercise 3M**

1. 13	**2.** 17	**3.** 8	**4.** 0	**5.** 24	**6.** 12
7. 3	**8.** 3	**9.** 9	**10.** 5	**11.** 1	**12.** $\frac{1}{2}$
13. 25	**14.** 0	**15.** 6	**16.** 20	**17.** 10	**18.** $\frac{2}{3}$
19. 24	**20.** 4	**21.** 120			

Page 239 **Exercise 3E**

1. 38	**2.** 0	**3.** 3	**4.** 100	**5.** 16	**6.** $\frac{1}{3}$
7. 1	**8.** 84	**9.** $\frac{1}{9}$	**10.** 5	**11.** 103	**12.** 160
13. 315	**14.** 27	**15.** 0	**16.** 500	**17.** 19	**18.** 60
19. 70	**20.** 0	**21.** $\frac{1}{8}$	**22.** 9.6	**23.** 0.2	**24.** −60
25. $\frac{1}{6}$	**26.** 877	**27.** 0.27	**28.** 1595	**29.** $\frac{1}{3}$	**30.** −0.075

Page 240 **Exercise 4M**

1. 3	**2.** 7	**3.** 4	**4.** 1	**5.** 3	**6.** 9
7. 5	**8.** $\frac{7}{9}$	**9.** $\frac{2}{5}$	**10.** $\frac{1}{2}$	**11.** 6	**12.** 20
13. 8	**14.** $\frac{2}{7}$	**15.** 7	**16.** $\frac{1}{3}$	**17.** 50	**18.** $\frac{4}{9}$
19. 20	**20.** $4\frac{1}{3}$	**21.** 0	**22.** $\frac{4}{5}$	**23.** 6	**24.** $\frac{2}{3}$

Page 241 **Exercise 4E**

1. 9	**2.** 6	**3.** 1	**4.** 12	**5.** 0	**6.** $\frac{4}{7}$

7. 14   **8.** $\frac{3}{5}$ **9.** $\frac{1}{4}$ **10.** $\frac{1}{13}$ **11.** $\frac{1}{4}$ **12.** $\frac{2}{3}$

13. $2\frac{2}{5}$ **14.** 0   **15.** $2\frac{1}{2}$ **16.** 9   **17.** 201   **18.** $\frac{7}{9}$

19. 9   **20.** 45   **21.** $\frac{1}{50}$ **22.** $\frac{1}{4}$ **23.** $\frac{1}{8}$ **24.** $\frac{2}{3}$

Page 241   *Exercise 5M*

1. 10   **2.** 7   **3.** 5   **4.** 30   **5.** $3\frac{2}{3}$ **6.** $2\frac{2}{5}$

7. 2   **8.** $\frac{5}{6}$ **9.** $2\frac{2}{5}$ **10.** $\frac{1}{4}$

Page 242   *Exercise 5E*

1. (a) 45   (b) 30   (c) 35   **2.** 27°   **3.** 8 cm

4. 5 cm   **5.** 7 cm   **6.** 6 g   **7.** (a) 19   (b) 21

8. A:65 kg, B:15 kg, C:45 kg, D:8 kg   **9.** 3.5 cm   **10.** 16, 17, 18, 19   **11.** 6

12. (a) $3x + 2$ (b) 6   **13.** 31 km   **14.** 52°, 64°, 64°   **15.** 87°, 93°, 87°, 93°

Page 244   *Exercise 6M*

1. $2x + 6$ **2.** $6x + 24$ **3.** $3x + 27$ **4.** $5x + 40$ **5.** $4x - 28$ **6.** $2x - 16$

7. $9x - 36$ **8.** $6x - 48$ **9.** $4x + 4y$ **10.** $7a + 7b$ **11.** $3m - 3n$ **12.** $10x + 15$

13. $24x - 42$ **14.** $8a + 4b$ **15.** $9m + 18n$ **16.** $4x + 12y$ **17.** $8m + 2n$ **18.** $35x - 21$

19. $24 - 8x$ **20.** $24 - 12x$ **21.** $15a + 25b$ **22.** $pq + pr$ **23.** $mn - mp$ **24.** $ab + ac$

25. $ab - ae$ **26.** $xy + 3x$ **27.** $mn - 6m$ **28.** $xy - 9x$ **29.** $pq - 5p$ **30.** $ac + 7a$

31. $de + 8d$ **32.** $a^2 + 4a$ **33.** $m^2 - 6m$ **34.** $p^2 - 2p$ **35.** $x^2 + 9x$ **36.** $7a - a^2$

37. $2x + xy$ **38.** $10a + 15$ **39.** $27m - 18$ **40.** $24x - 6$ **41.** $32n + 28$ **42.** $4b - b^2$

Page 245   *Exercise 6E*

1. $5x + 14$ **2.** $7x + 21$ **3.** $7x + 12$ **4.** $11x + 34$ **5.** $10x + 33$ **6.** $13x + 16$

7. $37x + 30$ **8.** $10x$ **9.** $14x + 20$ **10.** $13x + 8$ **11.** $29x + 16$ **12.** $11x + 24$

13. $6x + 6$ **14.** $21x + 1$ **15.** $22x + 8$ **16.** $34x + 6$ **17.** $18x + 2$ **18.** $31x + 2$

19. $36x + 21$ **20.** $48x + 6$ **21.** (a) $12x + 58$ (b) $17x + 48$ (c) $24x + 76$

Page 246   *Check Yourself on Sections 4.5 and 4.6*

1. (a) -4 (b) -7 (c) -3 (d) -2 **2.** (a) -15 (b) 8

     (c) -3 (d) 32   **3.** (a) $4m$ (b) $2ab + a$ (c) 6   (d) $15mn$

     (e) 28   (f) 4   **4.** (a) 10   (b) 30   (c) $3\frac{1}{2}$ (d) $\frac{1}{5}$

5. (a) $5x + 35$ (b) $np - 3n$ (c) $x^2 + 8x$ (d) $18x + 12$ (e) $11x + 27$

Page 247 **Unit 4 Mixed Review**

Part one

1. £42

2. £27

3. True

4. 5.7 cm

5. (a) $5x - 15$

(b) $6x + 12$

6. 48

7. (a) 5

(b) 56

(c) $\dfrac{3}{4}$

8. £750.40

9. $\dfrac{7}{25}$

10. 3960 g

11. 3.2

12. 17

13.

15. 10 minutes

16. £4 999 998

17. 500 g

Part two

1. £5.50

2. 0.63

3. $n(n + 4) = n^2 + 4n$

4. (a) $\dfrac{7}{8}$ (b) 18   (c) $1\dfrac{1}{2}$

5. 694.008 cm^2

6. $x = 78° \to 79°$, $y = 59°$

7. 12.5 minutes

8. $19x + 18$

9. 67.5%

10. 2.5

11. £56.93

13. 39

14. £624

15. A by 1

16. 348 945

17. 12

18. (a)

-3	4	-1
2	0	-2
1	-4	3

(b)

-3	-5	5
7	-1	-9
-7	3	1

(c)

3	0	-4	-9
-10	-3	1	2
-7	-6	-2	5
4	-1	-5	-8

Page 250 **Puzzles and Problems 4**

Cross numbers without clues

1.

3	7	5		3	7
0		1	2	7	4
8	2	8		4	
5		1	6	2	5
1	8		9		3
3	7	1	2	5	

2.

3	8	2		3	1
7		7	9	7	3
5	8	2		3	
0		5	1	0	4
4	7		7		5
1	2	7	8	5	

3.

8	2	5	3	3	6	4
7		3	2	7		4
6	3		4	4	8	8
4	3	6		5	7	3
3	7	5	6	1	5	
6		1	8	2		6
4	2	5	3	4	6	4

4.

3	4	4	6	2		2	7
4		5	3	0	4		1
7	4	5	6	2		5	4
3	1	1		4	8	3	
	2	8	5		1	6	1
5		5	3	6	0		1
3	6		8	4	7	6	2
5	3	7	0		2	9	7

5.

5	6	3	2	4		5	6
6		2	8	3	1		0
4	7	1	8	5		3	7
7	6	8		9	5	2	
	9	0	2		6	2	7
7		2	8	7	3		4
6	9		5	2	3	1	4
2	8	4	6		7	6	1

6.

2	4	6	8	1		5	3	5	1
8	3		2	4	5	8		5	3
5	5		5	6	3			5	6
	1	2	1		2	4	5	7	
1		4		2	1	7			2
3	3	5		3		3	8	6	4
4	4	6	2		8		2	1	6
9	5	1	2		2	1			8
	5			2	4	6	3	9	1
9	1	7		2	1	5	6	1	3

Page 252   ***The Königsberg Problem***

1. It cannot be done

Page 253   ***Mental Arithmetic Test 1***

1. 5, 7 or 35	**2.** 63	**3.** £7.70	**4.** 25 cm^2	**5.** 2010
6. 20	**7.** 6.3	**8.** 1	**9.** £8.97	**10.** 27
11. £1	**12.** 50, 10, 5, 2	**13.** £11.95	**14.** 1h 25 min	**15.** 80 000
16. 1 500 000 000	**17.** 4.05	**18.** 12	**19.** 790 mm	**20.** 8
21. 6	**22.** 240 cm	**23.** £55	**24.** 37	**25.** 64

Page 253   ***Mental Arithmetic Test 2***

1. £10 000	**2.** 24 cm^2	**3.** False	**4.** 295 cm	**5.** 6:35
6. 105	**7.** Thursday	**8.** 40%	**9.** 20, 20, 20, 5 or 50, 5, 5, 5	
10. £1 800 000	**11.** 121	**12.** 105°	**13.** $12\frac{1}{2}$	**14.** 7
15. £9.40	**16.** 64%	**17.** 90 cm	**18.** 499 mm	**19.** 250
20. 9:20	**21.** £66	**22.** 120°	**23.** 100 000	**24.** 100
25. 66				

Unit 5

Page 255 **Exercise 1M**

1. (a) 90° CW   (b) 180°   (c) 90° ACW   (d) 90° ACW   (e) 45° CW   (f) 180°
11. 90° CW   **12.** 90° ACW   **13.** 180°   **14.** 90° ACW   **15.** 180°   **16.** 90° ACW

Page 256 **Exercise 1E**

5. (a) U   (b) T   (c) R   (d) T   (e) T

Page 258 **Exercise 2M**

1. 3   **2.** No   **3.** 2   **4.** No   **5.** No   **6.** 2   **7.** 4   **8.** 2
9. 5   **10.** 8   **11.** 5   **12.** No   **13.** 6   **14.** 6   **15.** 3   **16.** 4

Page 258 **Exercise 2E**

1. (a) Yes   (b) 4

2.
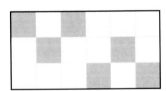

3.
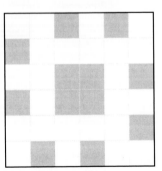

4.
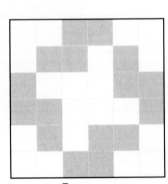

5.
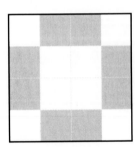

6.
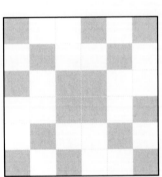

7.

8. Order 16

Page 260 **Exercise 1M**

1. One line   **2.** One line   **3.** Four lines   **4.** Four lines   **5.** One line
6. Four lines   **8.** (a) E, H, T,   (b) N, Z, H   (c) H
9. (a) No   (b) Yes   **10., 11., 12.** Own designs

Page 261   Exercise 1E

1. (3, 10); $x = 2$, $y = 8$ **2.** (10, –1); $x = 7$, $y = 1$ **3.** (10, –3); $x = 7\frac{1}{2}$, $y = -2\frac{1}{2}$

4. (5, –6)   **5.** (4, –8)   **6.** (–4, 7); $x = -6$, $y = 7$

7. (–3, 3); $x = 0$, $y = 0$, $y = x$, $y = -x$ **8.** (4, –2)   **9.** (–1, –8), (–7, –2), (–9, –8)

10. (–4, 4), (–2, 4), (0, 8)   **11.** (9, 9), (9, 6); $x = 7\frac{1}{2}$, $y = 7\frac{1}{2}$, $x + y = 15$

Page 262   Exercise 2M

1. 3   **2.** 4   **3.** 5   **4.** 9   **5.** 9   **6.** 10

Page 262   Exercise 2E

1. 2   **2.** 3   **3.** 3   **4.** 6   **5.** 28   **6.** 17

7. $17\frac{1}{2}$ **8.** $24\frac{1}{2}$

Page 263   Exercise 3M

1. 19 possible designs

Page 264   Exercise 3E For discussion/investigation

Page 266   Exercise 1M

2. (a) 2 right, 3 down   (b) 5 right, 3 up   (c) 4 left, 1 up   (d) 7 left
3. (e) 2 right, 4 down

Page 267   Exercise 1E

1. (a) E   (b) C   (c) F   (d) E
2. 1 right, 2 up; 5 right; 3 down; 2 left; 2 up; 2 left; 1 left, 2 down; 1 left, 1 up.
3. (a) 2 units right (b) BC
    (c) 90° clockwise about B, 90° anticlockwise about C, 180° about mid-point of BC

Page 267   Check Yourself on Units 5.1, 5.2 and 5.3

2. (a) 2   (b) 6   (c) 3   (d) 2   (e)

3.

5. (b) (i) 3 units right and 2 units up   (ii) 2 units left and 1 unit up   (iii) 4 units up

Page 269   **Exercise 1M**

1. 16, 20, 24, 28

2. (a) 3, 6, 9, 12, 15 (b) 7, 14, 21, 28, 35 (c) 2, 4, 6, 8, 10 (d) 10, 20, 30, 40, 50

3. (a) 1, 2, 3, 6 (b) 1, 3, 5, 15 (c) 1, 2, 3, 4, 6, 9, 12, 18, 36

(d) 1, 2, 4, 5, 10, 20, 25, 50, 100

4. (a) 48 (b) 20 (c) 111 (d) 1

5. 2, 3, 5, 7, 11, 13, 17, 19   **6.** 11, 31, 71   **7.** $2 + 3 = 5, 2 + 5 = 7$ (+ many others)

8. 4, 9   **9.** 2   **10.** 6, 12, 18 etc   **11.** 15, 30, 45 etc

12. (a) 4, 8, 12, 16, 20, 24 (b) 5, 10, 15, 20, 25, 30 (c) 20

13. (a) 3, 6, 9, 12, 15, 18, 21 (b) 7, 14, 21, 28, 35, 42, 49 (c) 21

14. 6   **15.** (a) 3 (b) 12 (c) 4

Page 271   **Exercise 2M**

1. (a) 9 (b) 20 (c) 3 (d) 12 (e) 24

(f) 15 (g) 18 (h) 15 **2.** (a) $\frac{3}{5}$ (b) $\frac{5}{7}$

(c) $\frac{1}{3}$ (d) $\frac{7}{8}$ (e) $\frac{13}{20}$ (f) $\frac{7}{10}$ (g) $\frac{1}{3}$

(h) $\frac{19}{35}$ **3.** (a) 0.3 (b) 0.25 (c) 0.8 (d) 0.12

(e) 0.09 **4.** (a) 20% (b) 15% (c) 4% (d) 45%

(e) 22% (f) 44% **5.** (a) $\frac{1}{5}$ (b) $\frac{9}{10}$ (c) $\frac{3}{100}$

(d) $\frac{11}{100}$ (e) $\frac{43}{100}$ (f) $\frac{3}{100}$ (g) $\frac{3}{20}$ (h) $\frac{17}{20}$

(i) $\frac{6}{25}$ (j) $\frac{1}{20}$ **6.** (a) $33\frac{1}{3}\%$ (b) 40% (c) 75%

(d) 3% (e) $66\frac{2}{3}\%$ (f) 0.1% **7.** (a) $\frac{2}{5}, 0.4, 40\%$

(b) $\frac{3}{20}, 0.15, 15\%$ (c) $\frac{3}{25}, 0.12, 12\%$ (d) $\frac{4}{25}, 0.16, 16\%$ (e) $\frac{1}{25}, 0.04, 4\%$

8. (a) $60\%, 0.7, \frac{3}{4}$ (b) $\frac{1}{50}, 0.03, 5\%$ (c) $23\%, 0.3, \frac{3}{9}$ **9.** (a) 20%

(b) $\frac{11}{20}$ (c) 8% (d) $\frac{6}{25}$

Page 272   **Exercise 3M**

1. 322 **2.** 595 **3.** 621 **4.** 1248 **5.** 1960 **6.** 2952

7. 2375 **8.** 7704 **9.** (a) 375 (b) 561 (c) 1134 **10.** (a) 56

(b) 17 (c) 26 (d) 45 **11.** 5 **12.** 805 **13.** 1

14. 3388g **15.** 36

Page 272   ***Exercise 4M***

1. (a) 9.2   (b) 24.8   (c) 2.54   (d) 4.14   (e) 1.538   (f) 7.8

  (g) 17.6   (h) 13.7   **2.** (a) 6.54 + 1.73 = 8.27   (b) 4.75 + 4.35 = 9.10

  (c) 6.872 + 1.219 = 8.091   **3.** £18.24   **4.** 0.021   **5.** £1, 50p, 20p, 5p, 2p

6. (a) 6.89 – 1.32 = 5.57   **7.**

  (b) 8.73 – 3.26 = 5.47

  (c) 7.48 – 6.78 = 0.70

8. (a) 32.6   (b) 114

  (c) 41.5   (d) 120

  (e) 1.76   (f) 4.27

  (g) 1.653   (h) 0.042

9. (a) 10   (b) 1.7   (c) 1.6   (d) 0.854   (e) 1   (f) 0.02

10. 2.4   **11.** (a) 23.92   (b) 0.78   (c) 1.24   (d) 3.4   (e) 5.3

  (f) 8.61   (g) 1.42   (h) 48.12   **12.** £8.40

Page 274   ***Exercise 5M***

1. (a) 46   (b) 48   (c) 64   (d) 225   **2.** (a) $\frac{1}{7}$ (b) $\frac{1}{11}$

  (c) $\frac{1}{2}$ (d) 18   (e) $\frac{2}{3}$ (f) $\frac{7}{100}$ **3.** 27   **4.** 240

5. (a) £80   (b) £15   (c) £11.06   (d) 2 kg   (e) 1975.5   (f) 65

  (g) 18 g   (h) 21.4 cm   **6.** (a) 25%   (b) 40%   (c) $33\frac{1}{3}$%   (d) 2%

7. (a) £7.50   (b) 28 km   (c) £25.20   (d) £201.60   (e) 17.5 kg   (f) 220 miles

8. 900   **9.** (a) $0.15, \frac{1}{5}, 22\%, \frac{1}{4}$ (b) $0.05, \frac{1}{8}, 52\%, \frac{3}{5}$ (c) $0.17, 66\%, \frac{2}{3}, 0.7$

10. 18% of 300   **11.** 70.4   **12.** £141.50

Page 275   ***Exercise 1M***

1. $\frac{1}{2}$ **2.** (a) $\frac{1}{4}$ (b) $\frac{1}{8}$ (c) $\frac{1}{3}$ (d) $\frac{1}{2}$

3. (a) $\frac{3}{5}$ (b) $\frac{2}{5}$ **4.** (a) $\frac{1}{3}$ (b) $\frac{1}{3}$ **5.** (a) $\frac{1}{7}$ (b) $\frac{2}{7}$

6. Bag A   **7.** (a) $\frac{1}{9}$ (b) $\frac{4}{9}$ (c) $\frac{4}{9}$

Page 276   ***Exercise 1E***

1. (a) $\frac{1}{5}$ (b) $\frac{2}{5}$ **2.** (a) $\frac{1}{6}$ (b) $\frac{1}{2}$ (c) 0   **3.** (a) $\frac{1}{2}$ (b) $\frac{2}{5}$

4. (a) $\frac{1}{6}$ (b) $\frac{1}{3}$ **5.** (a) $\frac{1}{5}$ (b) 0   (c) $\frac{2}{5}$ **6.** $\frac{1}{150}$

7. (a) 1   (b) 0   **8.** $\frac{1}{55}$

Page 278   **Exercise 2M**

1. (a) $\frac{1}{13}$ (b) $\frac{1}{52}$ (c) $\frac{1}{4}$

2. (a) $\frac{1}{4}$ (b) $\frac{1}{2}$ (c) $\frac{1}{13}$ (d) $\frac{3}{13}$ (e) $\frac{1}{52}$

3. (a) $\frac{1}{20}$ (b) $\frac{1}{5}$ (c) $\frac{1}{5}$ (d) $\frac{1}{2}$ (e) $\frac{1}{4}$

4. (a) $\frac{5}{8}$ (b) $\frac{3}{8}$ (c) $\frac{1}{8}$ **5.** (a) $\frac{3}{11}$ (b) $\frac{5}{11}$ (c) $\frac{1}{11}$

6. (a) $\frac{5}{9}$ (b) $\frac{1}{3}$ (c) $\frac{1}{9}$ (d) $\frac{5}{11}$ **7.** $\frac{2}{3}$

8. (a) (i) $\frac{2}{11}$ (ii) $\frac{3}{11}$ (b) (i) $\frac{5}{11}$ (ii) $\frac{2}{11}$

9. (a) True; she has a $\frac{1}{6}$ chance, Ben has $\frac{1}{7}$ (b) False; chance for Sarah is $\frac{1}{2}$, but Ben's is $\frac{3}{7}$

   (c) False

Page 279   **Exercise 2E**

1. 1 red ball and 1 white ball   **2.** 2 white balls and 1 red ball   **3.** 2 red balls and 1 white ball

4. 1 red ball and 3 white balls   **5.** 6 black balls and 3 white balls   **6.** (a) $\frac{1}{9}$ (b) $\frac{2}{3}$

7. (a) $\frac{1}{8}$ (b) $\frac{1}{2}$ (c) 1   **8.** (a) $\frac{5}{7}$ (b) 0   (c) $\frac{4}{7}$

9. (a) ABC, ACB, BAC, BCA, CAB, CBA   (b) $\frac{1}{3}$ (c) $\frac{2}{3}$ (d) $\frac{2}{3}$

10. (a) True   (b) Unlikely as Monopoly involves more skill   **11.** (a) (i) $\frac{1}{12}$ (ii) $\frac{1}{10}$

   (b) (i) $\frac{1}{9}$ (ii) $\frac{1}{3}$ **12.** (a) $\frac{4}{39}$ (b) $\frac{4}{39}$ (c) 0   **13.** (a) $\frac{12}{49}$

   (b) $\frac{3}{49}$ **14.** $\frac{1}{7}$ **15.** $\frac{x}{x+y}$ **16.** (a) $\frac{w}{w+g+p}$ (b) $\frac{p}{w+g+p}$

   (c) $\frac{g+p}{w+g+p}$ **17.** Liz did the experiment properly.

Page 283   **Exercise 1M**

1. (a) 32 km   (b) 40 miles   (c) 16 km   **2.** (a) (i) £3.60   (ii) £1.40
   (iii) £3.20   (iv) £4.60   (b) (i) 390   (ii) 190   (iii) 330
   (iv) 70   (c) £3.80   **3.** (a) (i) 37°   (ii) 39°   (b) 10.00
   (c) 9.00 and 11.00   (d) 8.30 – 9.00   **4.** (a) 1400 m   (b) 1600 m   (c) 1200 m
   (d) 11.00 and 13.00   (e) 2400 m   (f) 30 minutes   (g) 3 h

Page 284 **Exercise 1E**

1. (a) (i) £200   (ii) £600   (iii) £400   (b) £200   **2.** (a) 50p   (b) 30 seconds

    (c) 75 seconds   **3.** (a) broken line is for bad weather   (b) about 44 m   (c) 30 mph

Page 285 **Exercise 2M**

  1. (a) about 2.6 pounds   (b) about 0.9 kg   **2.** (a) 25°C   (b) 59°F   **3.** (b) £23

Page 286 **Exercise 2E**

  1. (a) 100 km   (b) 1 h   (c) 08.15   (d) (i) 60 km/h   (ii) 80 km/h

  2. (a) 40 km   (b) 09.15   (c) (i) 100 km/h   (ii) 40 km/h   (d) $2\frac{1}{2}$ hours

  3. (a) $\frac{1}{2}$ hour   (b) 17.00   (c) 15.15   (d) (i) 20 km/h   (ii) 100 km/h

  4. (a) 15 miles   (b) 0930   (c) 50 m.p.h.   (d) 40 m.p.h.   **5.** (a) C

     (b) B   (c) A   (d) D   (e) E   **6.** 2030

  7. 1545   **8.** $1637\frac{1}{2}$ **9.** 1500   **10.** (a) 1100   (b) 1045

11. About 1325, 37 km from Kate's home   **12.** (a) Robber was caught   (b) 0234

13. (a) car C   (b) about 50 minutes

Page 289 **Check Yourself on Units 5.5 and 5.6**

1. (a) (i) $\frac{3}{7}$ (ii) $\frac{2}{7}$ (b) $\frac{3}{7}$ **2.** (a) 15°C   (b) October   (c) April and November

    (d) April, May   (e) 21°C   **3.** (a) 37.5 miles   (b) 32 km   **4.** 12.30

Page 292 **Exercise 1M**

1. (a) 8   (b) 10   (c) 11   (d) 9   (e) 12

    (f) 57   (g) 21   (h) 108   (i) 1   (j) 17

2. (a) T   (b) T   (c) T   (d) F   (e) T

    (f) F   (g) T   (h) T   **3.** (a) 70   (b) 90

    (c) 230   (d) 360   (e) 80   (f) 1280   (g) 250

    (h) 1890   (i) 300   (j) 190   **4.** (a) 1680   (b) 1720

    (c) 1690   (d) 1700   (e) 1720   **5.** (a) 600   (b) 300

    (c) 6100   (d) 900   (e) 700   (f) 2900   (g) 65 500

    (h) 200   (i) 1500   (j) 28 400   **6.** (a) 5000   (b) 1000

    (c) 8000   (d) 23 000   (e) 7000   (f) 1000   (g) 3000

    (h) 26 000   (i) 14 000   (j) 295 000   **7.** (a) 56 800   (b) 2000

    (c) 100   (d) 7200   (e) 900   (f) 9400   (g) 300

    (h) 100   (i) 800   **8.** (a) 34   (b) 81   (c) 216

    (d) 59   (e) 40   (f) 23   (g) 122   (h) 12

    (i) 23   (j) 156   (k) 6   (l) 21   **9.** (a) 163 cm

    (b) 160 cm   (c) 2 m

Page 293   ***Exercise 1E***

1. (a) 2.4   (b) 8.9   (c) 4.7   (d) 12.5   (e) 16.4   **2.** (a) 1.92 $\frac{1}{13}$

    (b) 4.07   (c) 10.00   (d) 65.37   (e) 14.04   **3.** (a) 18.8   (b) 3.6

    (c) 17.1   (d) 0.8   (e) 5.4   (f) 11.3   (g) 10.3   (h) 7.1

4. (a) 3.76   (b) 11.64   (c) 0.38   (d) 138.30   (c) 11.44   (f) 7.06

    (g) 6.58   (h) 5.31   **5.** (a) 9.3   (b) 59.5   (c) 0.8   (d) 129.8

    (e) 1.4   (f) 11.7   (g) 22.6   (h) 27.3   **6.** (a) 1.6   (b) 19.4

    (c) 0.2   (d) 2.2   (e) 1.2   (f) 4.6   (g) 74.6   (h) 7.9

7. (Teacher's note: Many 'ordinary' rulers are not very accurate! If necessary, allow for minor differences to the following answers.)

    (a) 8.2 cm   (b) 2.2 cm   (c) 10.9 cm   (d) 5.5 cm   (e) 12.8 cm

8. (a) (i) 5.0×3.6 cm   (ii) 6.1×3.9 cm   (b) (i) 18.0 cm^2 (ii) 23.8 cm^2

Page 295   ***Exercise 2M***

1. 1000   **2.** 70   **3.** 60   **4.** 200   **5.** 400   **6.** 30

7. 8000   **8.** 10 000   **9.** 30   **10.** 800 000   **11.** 150   **12.** 80

13. 60   **14.** 20   **15.** 1   **16.** 300   **17.** 0.6   **18.** 8000

19. £4000   **20.** £20

Page 295   ***Exercise 2E***

1. (a) £24   (b) £23.88   **2.** £80   **3.** (a) 120 cm^2 (b) 118.34 cm^2 **4.** £150

5. £4800   **6.** £300   **7.** (a) 48.99   (b) 1.96   (c) 214.2   (d) 15.33

    (e) 103.8   (f) 7.657   **8.** (a) 20.64   (b) 52.56   (c) 200.9   (d) 1.19

    (e) 9.13   (f) 0.14   **9.** (a) £16000 – £20000   (b) £2000 – £2500   **10.** £5 million

Page 297   ***Exercise 1M***

1. 2 cm, 4 cm   **2.** 3 m, 6 m   **3.** 7 m, 14 m   **4.** 3 cm, 6 cm   **5.** 4 cm, 8 cm

6. 8 cm, 16 cm   **7.** 1 m, 2 m   **8.** 9 cm, 18 cm

Page 299   ***Exercise 1E***

1. 2, 4, 12, 12.6 cm   **2.** 5, 10, 30, 31.4 cm   **3.** 4.5, 9, 27, 28.3 m

4. 15, 30, 90, 94.2 mm   **5.** 8, 16, 48, 50.3 km   **6.** 10, 20, 60, 62.8 m

7. 12.5, 25, 75, 78.5 m   **8.** 23, 46, 138, 144.5 mm   **9.** 25, 50, 150, 157.1 cm

10. 37, 74, 222, 232.5 m   **11.** 34, 68, 204, 213.6 km   **12.** 10, 20, 60, 62.8 mm

13. 226 cm   **14.** 157.1 cm   **15.** 18.8 km (1d.p.)

16. 22.0 mm (1d.p.)   **17.** 9.4 km (1d.p.)

Page 301   ***Exercise 2M***

1. 380.1 mm^2 **2.** 113.1 cm^2 **3.** 314.2 m^2 **4.** 452.4 cm^2 **5.** 1256.6 km^2

6. 5026.5 cm^2 **7.** 1520.5 mm^2 **8.** 530.9 cm^2 **9.** 706.9 m^2 **10.** 2827.4 cm^2

11. 1963.5 m^2 **12.** 3217.0 km^2 **13.** 2206.2 cm^2 **14.** 55.4 m^2 **15.** 855.3 cm^2

Page 302 **Exercise 2E**

1. 56.5 km²   **2.** 226.2 cm²   **3.** 201.1 m²   **4.** 530.9 mm²   **5.** 50.3 cm²
6. 7.1 m²   **7.** 314.2 cm²   **8.** 95.0 km²   **9.** C = 21.4 cm, A = 36.3 cm²
10. C = 201.1 m, A = 3217.0 m²   **11.** C = 37.7 cm, A = 113.1 cm²
12. C = 125.7 cm, A = 1256.6 cm²   **13.** 235.6 cm

Page 302 **Test yourself on Units 5.7 and 5.8**

1. (a) (i) 560   (ii) 2050   (iii) 70   (b) (i) 5.7   (ii) 9.2
(iii) 0.8   (iv) 5.4   **2.** (a) 150   (b) 40   (c) 10
(d) £60   **3.** (a) (i) 18.8 cm   (ii) 13.2 m   (iii) 28.3 cm
(b) (i) 28.3 cm²   (ii) 13.9 m²   (iii) 63.6 cm²

Page 303 **Mixed Review Part One**

1. 120 g   **2.** £35.42 or £35.43   **3.** (a) (i) 4   (ii) 13   (b) (i) order 8
(ii) order 13   **4.** 48   **5.** (a) 5 + 4 − 2 = 7 (b) (5 + 4) ÷ 3 = 3

(c) (5 + 1) ÷ (4−2) = $1\frac{1}{2}$ (d) (5 + 4 + 2) × 3 = 33   **6.** $\frac{4}{7}$ **7.** (a) 30
(b) 19   (c) 25   (d) 10   **8.** 3   **9.** (4, 5)
10. £5.40, £8.10   **11.** (a) 20°C   (b) 16°C   (c) 17.00 and 22.30   (d) 15.00
(e) 22.00   **12.** (2,8) (6,8) (2,0) (6, 0) (4, 2) (4, 6)   **13.** 105
14. (a) 5.35 + 3.74   (b) 7.98−3.83 = 4.15   (c) 43.7 + 26.3 = 70.0
15.

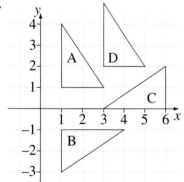

Page 305 **Part two**

1. (c) (i) (4,−2)   (ii) (4,4)   (iii) (−2,−2)   (iv) (0,−2)
2. £44.55   **3.** Con 115.2°, Lab 126°, Lib Dem 91.8°, Don't know 27°
4. 10 mins   **5.** 1032   **6.** 16 km   **7.** 1 green, 2 yellow, 3 blue
8. (a) 96 cm²   (b) 48 cm   (c) rotational symmetry, order 4
9. +1, ÷ 4 (Hint: notice that 7→7 and 11→11)   **10.** (a) various e.g 346 − 1, 690 ÷ 2
(b) e.g 460 ÷ 4   **11.** 184 cm   **12.** (a) 5.5   (b) 0.3   (c) 2.2
13. (a) $\frac{2}{6}$ (b) $\frac{2}{87}$ **14.** 320 secs = 5 min 20 sec   **15.** $\frac{10}{11}$
16. (a) 20.1 cm (1d.p.)   (b) 29.0 cm²

Page 308   **Puzzles and Problems 5**

Break the codes

1. γ ↑ ! ⊖ ⊥
   2 3 5 1 9

2. ♂ ♍ □ ⊙ ↑ ✳ ⊠ △ ♋ ⊠
   1 5 7 6 8 3 9 4 2 0

3. ♂ ♍ □ ⊙ ↑ ✳ ⊠ △ ♋ ⊠
   9 0 5 8 7 3 6 2 4 1

4. ♂ ♍ □ ⊙ ↑ ✳ ⊠ △ ♋ ⊠
   8 3 1 7 0 9 2 4 6 5

Apologies: Part (h) should be 'multiply' not 'add'.

Page 310   **Mental Arithmetic Test 1**

1. $\dfrac{7}{100}$	**2.** £57	**3.** equilateral	**4.** 4.7	**5.** three from 1,2,3,6
6. 24	**7.** 10	**8.** 3.5 cm	**9.** obtuse	**10.** 29
11. 20	**12.** £22	**13.** $\dfrac{2}{6} = \dfrac{1}{3}$	**14.** 60%	**15.** 360°
16. 28 cm	**17.** 16	**18.** same	**19.** 30	**20.** 8
21. £10 000	**22.** 85 cm	**23.** 3000 m	**24.** 90°	**25.** 35

Page 310   **Mental Arithmetic Test 2**

1. 220	**2.** 199	**3.** 1989	**4.** $\dfrac{1}{5}$	**5.** £1.44
6. 32	**7.** 75°	**8.** 1	**9.** none	**10.** 2.5
11. $\dfrac{5}{12}$	**12.** £4.08	**13.** 24	**14.** 207	**15.** 60
16. 48 miles	**17.** 30	**18.** 15	**19.** 3600	**20.** 12
21. False	**22.** 15	**23.** £5.50	**24.** 160	**25.** 999

Page 312   **Roman Numerals**

1. (a) 7   (b) 13   (c) 16   (d) 27   (e) 18

(f) 19   (g) 45   (h) 72   (i) 327   (j) 94

(k) 2006   (l) 949   **2.** (a) VIII   (b) XVII   (c) XXII

(d) LVIII   (e) XXXIX   (f) LXXXIV   (g) LXXVIII   (h) CXXIII

(i) CCCXXXIX   (j) MCCLXV   (k) MLXVI   (l) MMMCXCIV

4. (a) IX   (b) XVII   (c) XXX   (d) XXXIV   (e) XXXV

(f) LIII   (g) CCCXI   (h) X   (i) XXXVI   (j) CXXXIII

(k) XLII   (l) LXXXIV   (m) VIII   (n) V   (o) VI

(p) IV   (q) XL   (r) MCCCXXXIX

Unit 6

Page 313 **Exercise 1M**

1. (a) 16   (b) 7   (c) 5   (d) 36   (e) 81   (f) $\frac{1}{3}$

2. (a) 8   (b) 2   (c) 4   (d) 10   (e) $\frac{4}{5}$ (f) $\frac{2}{7}$ **3.** 6

4. (a) $\frac{4}{7}$ (b) $\frac{2}{13}$ (c) 8   (d) $\frac{3}{5}$ (e) 7   (f) $\frac{3}{7}$

5. (a) $\frac{1}{6}$ (b) $\frac{3}{8}$ (c) $\frac{1}{2}$ (d) $\frac{7}{10}$ (e) $\frac{7}{12}$ (f) $\frac{7}{8}$ **6.** $\frac{8}{7}=1\frac{1}{7}$

7. (a) 25   (b) 36   (c) $\frac{1}{4}$ (d) 0   (e) 100   (f) $\frac{1}{20}$

Page 314 **Exercise 1E**

1. (a) $\frac{3}{4}$ (b) $\frac{4}{5}$ (c) $\frac{7}{2}=3\frac{1}{2}$ (d) $\frac{7}{2}=3\frac{1}{2}$ (e) $\frac{1}{3}$ (f) $\frac{3}{2}=1\frac{1}{2}$

2. (a) 3   (b) 2   (c) 3   (d) 5   (e) 9   (f) 3

3. $n=5$, length = 17 cm, width = 5 cm   **4.** (a) $\frac{4}{5}$ (b) $\frac{1}{2}$ (c) $\frac{3}{2}=1\frac{1}{2}$

   (d) 7   (e) $\frac{11}{2}=5\frac{1}{2}$ (f) $\frac{1}{3}$ **5.** 23   **6.** $x=25°$; 80°, 45°, 110°, 125°

7. (a) 7   (b) $\frac{7}{9}$ (c) $\frac{5}{2}=2\frac{1}{2}$ (d) $\frac{11}{6}=1\frac{5}{6}$ (e) 4   (f) $\frac{3}{4}$

   (g) $\frac{5}{4}=1\frac{1}{4}$ (h) $\frac{5}{2}=2\frac{1}{2}$ (i) $\frac{1}{4}$

Page 315 **Exercise 1M**

1. (b) 3 times   **2.** 4 times   **3.** (c) 2 times, add 1   **4.** (c) 4 times, add 1
5. (b) is 4 more than the number of black squares   **6.** $s=3n$; $s=4n$; $s=2n+1$; $s=4n+1$

Page 317 **Exercise 2M**

1. (a) 6   (b) 12   (c) 60   **2.** (a) 7   (b) 15
   (c) 205   **3.** (a) 7, 14, 21, 28   (b) 4, 5, 6, 7   (c) 4, 7, 10, 13   (d) 24, 23, 22, 21
   (e) 11, 15, 19, 23   **4.** (a) $10n$ (b) $3n$ (c) $4n+1$ (d) $50n$
   (e) n^2 (f) $2n+6$ (g) $3n+8$ (h) $12n$
5. (a) M5 = 20, M6 = 24, N5 = 22, N6 = 26   (b) M15 = 60, N20 = 82
6. 3:(6, 6); 5:(10, 10); 40:(80, 80); 45:(90, 90)   **7.** (a) (10, 3)   (b) (100, 3)   (c) (101, 1)
   (d) (201, 1)   **8.** (a) (16, 4)   (b) (80, 4)   (c) (8000, 4)   **9.** (a) (4, 8)
   (b) (10, 20)   (c) (70, 141)   **10.** (a) (120, 2)   (b) (146, 4)   (c) (179, 3)
   (d) (201, 5)

Page 320 **Investigation – Count the Crossovers**

Part D: 20 lines have 190 crossovers $\left(\dfrac{20\times19}{2}\right)$

Part E: 2000 lines have 1 999 000 crossovers $\left(\dfrac{2000\times1999}{2}\right)$

Page 321 **Check Yourself on Sections 6.1 and 6.2**

1. (a) 9   (b) 56   (c) $\dfrac{5}{7}$ (d) $\dfrac{5}{6}$ (e) 9   (f) 6

2. (c) 2 times, add 6   (d) $g = 2b + 6$ (e) 43

Page 322   **Exercise 1M**

1. 590 cm	**2.** 9130 g	**3.** 0.7 kg	**4.** 3500 m	**5.** 4.3 cm
6. 0.7 m	**7.** 4000 ml	**8.** 2.5t	**9.** 2400 g	**10.** 0.3 m
11. 0.509 kg	**12.** 20 cm	**13.** 7400 ml	**14.** 0.06 kg	**15.** 62 000 ml
16. 3700 mm	**17.** 9500 mg	**18.** 0.003 kg	**19.** 4000 cm^3	**20.** 5020 g

Page 322   **Exercise 1E**

1. 48 inches	**2.** 18 feet	**3.** 112 pounds	**4.** 80 ounces	**5.** 5 feet
6. 4 ounces	**7.** 38 inches	**8.** 107 pounds	**9.** 8960 pounds	**10.** 77 inches
11. 8800 yards	**12.** 26 feet	**13.** 62 pounds	**14.** 12 pints	**15.** 5280 feet
16. 35840 ounces	**17.** 3.5 gallons	**18.** 77 pounds	**19.** 12 320 pounds	**20.** 140 inches

Page 323   **Exercise 2M**

1. 36 litres	**2.** 8.8 pounds	**3.** 45 litres	**4.** 10 miles	**5.** 20 cm
6. 20 kg	**7.** 10 feet	**8.** 48 km	**9.** 3 ounces	**10.** 160 cm
11. (a) 6 feet	(b) 350 ml	(c) 30 m	(d) 10 mm	(e) 25 g

12. (c) or a large van!   **13.** yes   **14.** 4 miles   **15.** £9.36

16. yes   **17.** 3 pounds   **18.** $\dfrac{1}{2}$ inch   **19.** (a) 2 feet, 0.55 m, 50 cm, 7 inches, 16 cm

(b) 1.1 pound, 0.48 kg, 450g, 0.4 kg, 9 ounces   **20.** 3(2.5 exactly)

Page 325   **Exercise 2E**

1. 5000	**2.** 300	**3.** 7 g	**4.** 2.325 kg	**5.** (a) 0.34 m^2
(b) 0.08 m^2	(c) 6.47 m^2	**6.** 112.32 litres	**7.** 14	**8.** (a) 2400 cm^2
(b) 66 700 cm^2	(c) 9.8 cm^2	**9.** (a) 384 hectares	(b) 32 hours	**10.** 0.6 seconds

Page 327   **Check Yourself on Section 6.3**

1. (a) 7650 m   (b) 40 cm   (c) 7.5 litres   **2.** (a) 8 ounces   (b) 22 pints

(c) 6 feet   **3.** (a) 5 cm   (b) £1.06   **4.** (a) P by 300 cm^2 (or 0.03 m^2)

(b) 0.125 mm

Page 328 **Exercise 1M**

1. (a) 35°　　　　(b) 55°　　　　(c) 70°　　　　(d) 15°　　　　(e) 120°
3. (d), (f)　　　　**4.** (a) 65°　　　　(b) 98°　　　　(c) 47°　　　　(d) 73°
5. (a) $a = 80°, b = 80°, c = 20°$　　　(b) $d = 75°, e = 30°$　(c) $f = 60°, g = 60°$　(d) $h = 63°, k = 54°$
6. No　　　　**7.** Yes　　　　**8.** 98°　　　　**9.** 30°

Page 329 **Exercise 1E**

1. $a = 95°, b = 95°$　　**2.** $c = 36°, d = 132°, e = 48°$　　**3.** $f = 27°$　　**4.** $g = 59°, h = 30°, k = 91°$
5. $m = 65°$　　　**6.** $n = 42°, 2n = 84°, 3n = 126°$　**7.** $p = 65°$　　**8.** $q = 110°, r = 40°$
9. 56°　　　**10.** 106°　　　　　　　　　**11.** 26°　　　**12.** 60°

Page 334 **Exercise 1M**

1. (a)

	faces	edges	vertices
A	6	12	8
B	6	12	8
C	5	9	6
D	8	18	12
E	4	6	4
F	5	8	5

(b) $F + V - 2 = E$

2. cuboids: 6 faces, 12 edges, 8 vertices　　　**3.** triangular prisms: 5 faces, 9 edges, 6 vertices
4. remaining shape: 7 faces, 15 edges, 10 vertices, piece cut off: 4 faces, 6 edges, 4 vertices
5. various answers　　　　　　　**6.** various answers

Page 336 **Exercise 2M**

1. (c) does not make a cube; (a), (b), (d), (e) do make cubes
2. (a) C　　　　　(b) F　　　　　(d) D　　　　　(e) C

Page 339 **Check Yourself on Sections 6.4 and 6.5**

1. (a) 80°　　　　(b) 48°　　　　(c) 68°　　　　　**2.** 3.7 cm
3. (a) 5 faces, 8 edges, 5 vertices　　　(b) 7 faces, 15 edges, 10 vertices
4. (a) and (c)

Page 340 **Unit 6 Mixed Review Part one**

1. 111　　　　　**2.** (a) BC　　　(b) JK　　　(c) H　　　　**3.** hemisphere
4. D　　　　　**5.** 0.999 m　　**6.** 64 g　　　**8.** (a) $n = 42$　　(b) $y = 8$
　(c) $x = \dfrac{5}{8}$　　(d) $w = \dfrac{4}{5}$　　(e) $p = \dfrac{1}{8}$　　(f) $a = 23$　　**9.** (c) 27
　(d) diagram number $\times$ 5 + 2　　**10.** 7000　　**11.** 56°　　**12.** 240 g

13. 0.4 cm = 4 mm   **14.** 90°
15. (a) WE NEED MORE SUMS   (b) HAVE A NICE DAY
    (c) SPURS ARE RUBBISH   (d) PLEASE SET MORE WORK

Page 342   ***Part two***

1. (a) 470 cm   (b) 0.063 kg   (c) 48 inches   (d) 0.36 km
    (e) 8000 ml   (f) 32 ounces   (g) 4.5 cm   (h) 15 feet   (i) 7600 g
2. (a) 65 536   (b) 4 194 304   **3.** 37°   **4.** £637
5. (a) $y = \dfrac{14}{3} = 4\frac{2}{3}$ (b) $x = 5$ (c) $x = 9$
6. $a = 6, b = 4, c = 5, d = 6, e = 4, f = 5$ **7.** 2.9 g
8. (a) C5 = 28, D5 = 31   (b) C10 = 58, D30 = 181
9. Lana by 0.5 cm   **11.** 0.08 mm   **12.**
13. £13   **15.** (a) 69°   (b) 36°

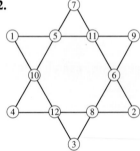